UCET Profiles
1999-2000

Published by
The Universities Council for the Education of Teachers
(Registered Charity No. 275082)
58 Gordon Square, London WC1H ONT
Tel: 0171 580 8000
Fax: 0171 323 0577
Email: r.klassen@ioe.ac.uk
Website: http://www.ucet.ac.uk

CONTENTS

INTRODUCTION

The Universities Council for the Education of Teachers (UCET) speaks on all matters concerning the education, training and professional development of teachers, and on educational research. Its members are the Departments, Schools and Institutes of Education in universities and university-sector colleges in England, Wales and Northern Ireland. It is an independent professional organisation, funded solely by its members. UCET contributes to the educational debate from its specialist position within Higher Education. It supports all appropriate moves to enhance the quality and status of the teaching profession.

UCET now has 85 members, and this publication provides a very brief profile of the provision and interest of each of its member institutions. Detailed information regarding these institutions may be found on their websites, which can be accessed via the UCET website, www.ucet.ac.uk.

The information in this publication has been provided by the institutions concerned.

Note: A few members were unable to provide us with their revised entry in time for inclusion. Details may, however, be obtained from their websites (accessible through the UCET website - www.ucet.ac.uk).

ANGLIA

Anglia Polytechnic University
School of Education
Sawyer's Building
Bishop Hall Lane
CHELMSFORD   CM1 1SQ

Tel:	01245 493131
Fax:	01245 490835
Email:	l.ede@anglia.ac.uk
Website:	www.anglia.ac.uk

Contact Person: Lesley Ede

Directions: Road: Exit from M25. Travel along A12 to A1016 to Chelmsford. Cross first roundabout, turn left at second, into Waterhouse Lane. Cross traffic lights into Parkway, follow one-way system and turn first right into Rectory Lane. Turn left at roundabout into Bishop Hall Lane. Rail: Chelmsford station. Turn left out of station and left at mini roundabout into Victoria Road. Continue down to traffic lights and turn left. Rivermead Campus is at the end of this road.

Staff:		
	Dean of School:	Ms Rebecca Bunting
	Professors:	4
	Other teaching staff:	30 f/t; 4 p/t
	Research staff & students:	1 reader, 70 PhD students

Overall FTE students in 1999/2000: 800

COURSES

ITE Primary: 1-year PGCE, age 5-11 (45); 3-year BA QTS, age 5-11 (95).
ITE Secondary: 1-year PGCE (96) in Art, English, MFL, Science; 2-year BA Hons QTS in Art with Education (20), French with Education (18), Science with Education (11).
ITE Post-Compulsory: PGCE in Teaching and Learning in HE and FE; MA in Teaching and Learning in HE and FE.
CPD / Higher Degrees: MA; EdD; MPhil; PhD; postgraduate certificates and diplomas.
Other Courses: Israeli Summer University, BA in Education (non-ITE).

PARTNERSHIPS

The School of Education has partnership arrangements for ITT and CPD with a range of LEAs, including Essex, Suffolk, Southend and Thurrock, in line with the University's regional mission.

MAIN RESEARCH AND DEVELOPMENT INTERESTS

- Evaluation of School-based Teacher Education
- Induction of Newly Qualified Teachers
- Experiential Learning
- Interprofessional Programmes
- Professional Partnerships
- Learning and Teaching in Higher Education
- Impact of Continuing Professional Development of Teachers

BATH

University of Bath
Department of Education
Claverton Down
BATH   BA2 7AY

Tel: 01225 826725
Fax: 01225 826113
Email: education@bath.ac.uk
Website: www.bath.ac.uk/departments/education

Contact Person: Mrs Jan Berridge, Secretary to Head of Department

Directions: Road: Exit Junction 18 from M4 onto A46. Follow directions to Bath (about 7 miles). Continue on A46 into Bath as it joins the A4. Follow signposts in Bath to the University. The Department of Education is on the north of the University campus in Building 1 West North. Rail: Bath Spa; 5-10 minutes by taxi.

Staff: Head of Department: Dr William Scott
         Professors: 3
         Other teaching staff: 27 f/t; 5 p/t
         Research staff & students: 104

Overall FTE students in 1999/2000: 450

COURSES

ITE KS 2/3:   1-year PGCE, age 7-14 (30), in English, Maths, Science.
ITE Secondary: 1-year PGCE (170) in English, History, Maths, MFL, Biology, Chemistry, Earth Science, Environmental Science, Physics, PE, Geography, IT.
CPD / Higher Degrees: 1-year f/t or p/t MA in Education - specialisation is possible in Educational Technology, Educational Management, International Education, Environmental Education, Language in Education; Advanced Certificates/Diplomas (Certificate and Diploma courses are run in partnership with local schools); EdD by tutored units and a research enquiry; MPhil; PhD; MSc in Social Research.

PARTNERSHIPS

The University is a founder member of Gloucestershire and Wiltshire Inservice Support for Teachers (GWIST), which is a partnership of three LEAs and two

HE institutions. GWIST is involved on a national basis in supporting the development of practising teachers, senior managers and head teachers, as well as meeting schools' and teachers' professional needs on a regional basis. The Department of Education has active links with all local LEAs and its PGCE in Partnership course involves working with over 80 schools in the local authorities within a 50 mile radius of Bath. These schools are represented on the Department's PGCE Policy Committee and school mentors and senior school tutors are full members of the PGCE Board of Examiners. All the Department's research groups (Professional Learning & Development, International & Comparative Education, Education Policy Innovation & Change, Culture & Environment) work directly with schools and teachers on a research, consultancy and professional development basis and aspects of the Department's MA programmes are taught in partner schools. In addition, the Centre for the study of Education in an International Context has extensive partnerships with International Schools across the world.

MAIN RESEARCH AND DEVELOPMENT INTERESTS

- Action Research
- Assessment & Evaluation
- Curriculum Studies
- Teacher Education
- Education / Industry Links
- Educational Technology
- Environmental Education
- Learning in Science & Mathematics
- Management in Education
- Teaching & Learning Processes in the Classroom
- Curriculum Evaluation
- School Improvement & School Effectiveness
- Mentoring
- Differential Learning
- Education & Sustainable Development
- Culture & Learning
- Language & Learning
- International & Comparative Education
- Educational Policy
- Innovation & Change
- Distance Learning

BATH SPA

Bath Spa University College
Newton Saint Loe
BATH   BA2 9BN

Tel:	01225 875875
Fax:	01225 875444
Email:	enquiries@bathspa.ac.uk
Website:	www.bathspa.ac.uk

Contact Person: Ms Christine Eden

Directions: Leave A4 Bath-Bristol road at Globe Inn roundabout. University College is signposted.

Staff: Head of Department: Ms Christine Eden

No current information submitted for this edition. Please contact Bath Spa University College directly or refer to their website.

QUEEN'S BELFAST

The Queen's University of Belfast
Graduate School of Education
BELFAST BT7 1HL

Tel: 028 9033 5941
Fax: 028 9023 9263
Email: education@qub.ac.uk
Website: www.qub.ac.uk/edu

Contact Person: Mrs M Rea or Mrs C Gribben

Directions: The University is one mile south of the City Centre on University Road. The Graduate School of Education's main site is at 69/71 University Street, ca. 100 metres from the main University Campus.

Staff: <u>Head of School:</u>   Professor John Gardner
          <u>Teaching staff:</u>   19 f/t
          <u>Research staff:</u>   6

Overall FTE students in 1999/2000: 400

COURSES

ITE Secondary: 1-year PGCE (190) in Maths, English, Sciences, MFL, IT/Computing, Politics.
CPD / Higher Degrees: P/t masters-level modular courses for an Advanced Certificate; Advanced Diploma, MEd, MSc; specialist programmes are available in Educational Management, Educational Psychology, Educational Studies, Guidance & Counselling, MFL, Primary Education, SEN; a f/t or p/t degree of Doctor of Education (EdD) in Educational Policy & Management; Certificates and Diplomas in Professional Development.

PARTNERSHIPS

The PGCE course at Queen's is based on partnerships with local schools and colleges, which have developed over some 40 years. These partnerships are not based on contractual arrangements but the schools, the University and the student teachers all have clearly defined roles based upon mutual trust, openness and team-work. The strength of these long-standing relationships provide the basis for joint activities during the induction, early inservice and continuing professional development of serving teachers. These include a variety of challenging courses up to taught doctorate level.

MAIN RESEARCH AND DEVELOPMENT INTERESTS

- Education in Divided Societies
- School Improvement & Effectiveness
- Assessment & Measurement
- Under-achievement in Schooling
- Information Technology in Education
- School Exclusions
- Languages in the Curriculum
- Children at Risk
- Science Education

OTHER SPECIAL FEATURES

The School has several specialist centres:
- The Centre for Modern Language Teaching
- The Northern Ireland Centre for Information on Language Teaching & Research
- The Centre for Educational Measurement

BIRMINGHAM

University of Birmingham
School of Education
Edgbaston
BIRMINGHAM B15 2TT

Tel: 0121 414 4831
Fax: 0121 414 7444
Email: h.r.thomas@bham.ac.uk
Website: www.bham.ac.uk/education

Contact Person: Professor Hywel Thomas

Directions: Road: On Bristol Road (A38) two and a half miles south-west of city centre. The School of Education building is on the corner of Edgbaston Park Road and Pritchatts Road. Map available on request. Rail: Birmingham New Street. Local trains run to University Station at ca. 15 minutes intervals.

Staff: Head of School: Professor Hywel Thomas
              Professors: 10
              Other teaching staff: 46 f/t; 13 p/t
              Research staff/students: 13/295

Overall FTE students in 1999/2000: 964

COURSES

ITE Secondary: 1-year PGCE (278) in Sciences, Maths, MFL, English, History Geography, RE, PE; 2-year f/t course in Maths (20).
CPD / Higher Degrees: AdCert, BPhil, PGCert, PGDip, MEd, MA, f/t or p/t; f/t and p/t courses in Teaching & Learning, Management for Learning, ICT, SEN; MPhil, EdD, PhD by research.
Available through distance learning: Education in Visual Impairment, Hearing Impairment, Speech & Language Difficulties, Emotional & Behavioural Difficulties, Autism, Learning Difficulties (moderate and severe), Multi-sensory Impairment, Bilingualism in Education.

PARTNERSHIPS

Partnerships exist with 60 schools for PGCE (ITT) Secondary courses. A number of the CPD courses noted above are developed and offered in partnership with schools and local education authorities through outreach teaching.

MAIN RESEARCH AND DEVELOPMENT INTERESTS

The School's research and development work is organised across three areas: Management & Policy, Curriculum & Teaching, Special Education & Educational Psychology. In the 1996 national Research Assessment Exercise the School maintained the 5A rating achieved in 1992. It is a rating which recognises the international standing of research work in the School and that all staff are research active.

OTHER SPECIAL FEATURES

Westhill College is accredited by the University for education courses.

BISHOP GROSSETESTE

Bishop Grosseteste College
Newport
LINCOLN LN1 3DY

Tel: 01522 527347
Fax: 01522 530243
Email: emb@bgc.ac.uk
Website: www.bgc.ac.uk

Contact Person: Professor Eileen Baker

Directions: Road: A46 Lincoln by-pass Newark to Grimsby, exit 'Lincoln North' (roundabout A46/A15) turning south with Cathedral in view. First roundabout straight ahead, the College is situated immediately on your left (within the city of Lincoln and ca. 3/4 mile due north of the Cathedral).

Staff: Head of Institution: Professor Eileen Baker
             Teaching staff: 32.3 f/t; 6.7 p/t

Overall FTE students in 1998/99: 870

COURSES

ITE Primary: 3-year BA Hons, age 3-11 Primary Education; 4-year BA/BSc Hons QTS, age 5-11, in named subject; PGCE, age 3-11.
CPD / Higher Degrees: Short courses; Diploma; Certificate; MA; MEd; MPhil; PhD (awarded by University of Hull); MBA

PARTNERSHIPS

ITT: Weekly visits by tutors sustain close partnership arrangements with ca. 300 schools in ca. eight LA areas.
CPD: A variety of kinds of contacts with local and distant LEAs, increasingly for more than one year.

MAIN RESEARCH AND DEVELOPMENT INTERESTS

* EY
* Literacy (primary)
* Numeracy (primary)
* Gender in Primary Subjects
* Primary Science
* School Management

OTHER SPECIAL FEATURES

Significant overseas commitments in a variety of locations, in particular 'interactive education' (Balkans) and CPD (Pakistan).

University of Brighton
School of Education
Falmer
BRIGHTON   BN1 9PH

Tel: 01273 643395
Fax: 01273 643555
Email: m.carroll@bton.ac.uk
Website: www.bton.ac.uk

Contact Person: Mrs Maggie Carroll

Directions: Road: Take the Brighton by-pass off the A23, signposted Lewes and the Universities. At end of by-pass remain in the inside lane past the University of Sussex. Turn right round the roundabout and continue over the bridge. Take the first turning right, leading to the University of Brighton, Falmer Campus. The Faculty of Education and Sport is located in part at Falmer. Rail: Brighton, then change to the South Coast Line and Falmer Station is a 7-minute train journey from Brighton.

Staff: Head of School: Mrs Maggie Carroll
             Professors: 3
             Other teaching staff: 50 f/t; ca. 50 p/t
             Research staff & students: 15

Overall FTE students in 1999/2000: 2300 (ITE and CPD)

COURSES

ITE Primary: 1-year PGCE - Early and Later Years routes (46); 4-year BA Hons QTS - Early and Later Years routes (117) in Art, Advanced Early Years, D&T, English, Geography, History, PE, RE, Science, IT.
ITE KS 2/3: 4-year BA Hons QTS in D&T (15), Maths (14), English (21), Science (14), MFL (8), IT (7), Geography (8), PE (15), RE (10).
ITE Secondary: 1-year PGCE (18-month p/t variant also available) in Art (88), D&T (31), IT (26), MFL (10), English (20), Business Education (20), RE (20), PE/Dance (30); p/t PGCE in Maths (3); 2-year Conversion PGCE in Maths (3), Science (3); 2-year BA Hons QTS in Business Education (11), D&T Education (16), Maths Education (6), MFL (8), Science Education (6); 4-year BA Hons QTS in D&T (15), Business Education with IT (12), PE (112).

CPD / Higher Degrees: 1-3 year p/t CertHE Applied Education Studies (24); 1-5 year DipHE Professtional Education Studies (30); 1-5 year p/t Diploma in Youth & Community (20); 1-5 year Diploma in RE (55); 1-5 year p/t BA RE Studies (10); 1-5 year Professional Education Studies (30); 1-6 year p/t Postgraduate Certificate in Education Management (55); 1-6 year p/t Postgraduate Certificate in Professional Education Studies (*); 1-6 year p/t Postgraduate Diploma in Education (*); 1-6 year p/t MA Learning in Organisations (8); 1-6 year f/t and p/t MA Education (*).
* total 50

PARTNERSHIPS

ITE: All schools are in partnership. Secondary model: University link tutor (not subject tutor) - school professional tutor - school subject mentor - subject specific visits in special circumstances. Primary model: University adviser - school mentor - school subject co-ordinator.

CPD: Good links established with East Sussex, West Sussex, Brighton & Hove. East Sussex and Brighton & Hove have Professional Development Centres on two University sites. Links are also established with Kent.

MAIN RESEARCH AND DEVELOPMENT INTERESTS

The Education Research Centre has four areas of research in which all research is located:
- Higher Education
- Literacies
- Cultural & Religious Dimensions
- Teaching & Learning (school-based)

OTHER SPECIAL FEATURES

- The University validates a CertEd (post-compulsory) at Brighton College of Technology and Hastings College of Art and Technology.
- The School of Education offers its MAEd programme in Mauritius.
- Some ITE students are able to engage in exchange programmes in Europe and North America.

University of Bristol
Graduate School of Education
35 Berkeley Square
BRISTOL BS8 1JA

Tel: 0117 928 9000
Fax: 0117 925 1537
Email: john.furlong@bris.ac.uk
Website: www.bris.ac.uk/depts/education

Contact Person: Professor John Furlong, Head of School

Directions: Road: From the North an Wales take Exit 16 from M5 and follow signs to City Centre. From London leave M4 for M32 at the end of which turn right and follow signs to Clifton. From the South West take Exit 19 and follow signs to City Centre and Clifton. The University Tower is an appropriate landmark; one of the two entrances to Berkeley Square faces it. Rail: Bristol Temple Meads; 10 minutes by taxi. Bristol Parkway is 6 miles outside the City; taxis are available (allow 25 minutes).

Staff: Head of School: Professor John Furlong
              Teaching staff: 45 f/t; 15 p/t
              Research staff: 12

Overall FTE students in 1999/2000: 500

COURSES

ITE Secondary: 1-year PGCE (223) in Art, History, RE, English, MFL, Geography, Maths, Music, Sciences; Games and Integrated Science offered as second subjects.
CPD / Higher Degrees: MPhil; PhD; EdD (combined research and teaching doctorate programme); modular f/t (1 year) or p/t (5 years max.) MEd/MSc, Advanced Diploma in Education; wide range of courses and specialist programmes in Management, Maths, Science, TEFL, Assessment, Guidance Counselling, Educational Psychology, SEN; wide range of short courses and workshops, study attachments and consultancy work for home and overseas clients; MSc; Diploma and certified Counselling programmes; MSc Information & Library Mangagement.

PARTNERSHIPS

54 Partnership schools.

MAIN RESEARCH AND DEVELOPMENT INTERESTS

Research has a high profile within the Graduate School of Education and there are substantial numbers of externally funded projects. Research is organised within eight centres, focusing on the common theme of Culture and Learning in Organisations. The Centres are:

- Learners in Society
- Learning, Knowing & Interactive Technologies
- Psychology & Language Studies
- Assessment Studies
- Professional Learning & Development
- Management & Policy Studies
- International & Comparative Studies
- Counselling & Learning

OTHER SPECIAL FEATURES

The University validates MEd courses at the Cheltenham and Gloucester College of Higher Education. The Document Summary Service (DSS) produces high quality summaries of DFEE documents for LEAs and Schools.

The School offers a range of short courses for teachers and others involved in education and schools (FPS). In 1999 a specialist strand of the EdD programme will be offered for Educational psychologists.

BRUNEL

Brunel University
School of Education
300 St Margaret's Road
TWICKENHAM   TW1 1PT

Tel: 020 8891 0121
Fax: 020 8744 2960
Email: school.education@brunel.ac.uk
Website: www.brunel.ac.uk/faculty/ed

Contact Person: Professor Steve Hodkinson

Directions: Underground: District Line to Richmond, then H37 bus or Piccadilly Line to Hounslow East, then H37 bus. Rail: St Margaret's Station, then 15 minutes walk or Richmond Station, then H37 bus. Bus: H37, bus stop on St Margaret's Road nearest junction with Talbot Road. Road: Chertsey Road (A316) to St Margaret's Road (A3004) north.

Staff: Head of School: Professor Steve Hodkinson
             Professors: 2
             Other teaching staff: 38 f/t; 10 p/t
             Research staff: 4

Overall FTE students in 1999/2000: 900

COURSES

ITE Primary: 3-year BA Hons QTS, age 5-11 (75); 1-year PGCE, age 5-11(54) - both courses with specialisms in English, Maths, Science.

ITE Secondary: 4-year BSc Hons QTS (25) in PE & Geography (2 years mainly subject study followed by 2 years teacher education study in partnership with schools); 1-year PGCE (218) in D&T, English, Geography, IT, Maths, MFL, PE, RE, Science; p/t 2-year PGCE by distance learning in Physics, Chemistry, Biology.

CPD / Higher Degrees: MA Education; Postgraduate Diploma (Education); Postgraduate Certificate (Education)(PgCert); MA/PgDip/PgCert Youth & Community; MA/PgDip in Primary Education, Secondary Education, SEN, Guidance & Counselling Skills, Severe Learning Difficulties, Information Technology in Education, Educational Management; EdD; MPhil; PhD.

PARTNERSHIPS

The School of Education believes that through learning, communities will promote a sense of common identity through active participation in shaping their future. Schools are invited into partnership to join in the further development of mutual benefits that can be derived. Our aim is to achieve sustainable school-focused initial teacher education through a process of negotiation and continual review and refinement which recognises the strengths which school and the university bring to partnership. The three principles of partnerships are: Mutual Benefit, Mutual Esteem, Shared Responsibility.

MAIN RESEARCH AND DEVELOPMENT INTERESTS

- Centre for Comparative Studies in Special Education
- Brunel Able Children Education Centre (BACE)
- Economics Education Research Centre
- Centre for Research in Teaching Thinking
- Science and Design Technology Research Unit
- Language in Education Research Unit
- Humanities Research Unit
- BFSS National Centre for Religious Education
- Centre for Study of Management & Leadership Education
- Education Policy & Practice in the European Union
- Centre for Youth Work Studies
- Professional Education (Teacher Education)

CAMBRIDGE

University of Cambridge
School of Education
17 Trumpington Street
CAMBRIDGE CB2 1QA

Tel: 01223 332888
Fax: 01223 332894
Email: educ-inst-tutorial@lists.cam.ac.uk
Website: www.educ.cam.ac.uk

Contact Person: Mrs Gillian Morley, Secretary of the Faculty

Directions: The Faculty of Education consists of the School of Education and Homerton College and is spread over three sites. Exit from M11 to A1309 down Trumpington Road towards City Centre. The *School of Education* at 17 Trumpington Street is on the right-hand side just before the Fitzwilliam Museum, or for the *Shaftesbury Road site* turn right into Brooklands Avenue just before the Botanic Gardens and right again. For *Homerton College* turn right just after Trumpington village into Long Road and then left into Hills Road; the College is on the left-hand side.

Staff: Head of School: Professor Donald McIntyre
Principal of Homerton College: Dr Kate Pretty
Teaching staff: 75 f/t; 11 p/t
Research staff & students: 44

Overall FTE students in 1999/2000: 1670

COURSES

ITE Primary: 1-year PGCE, age 3-8/7-11 (195); 4-year BEd QTS, age 3-8 with specialisms in Maths, Science, English, Drama, Geography, History, Music, RE, age 7-11 with specialisms in Geography, History (98).

ITE KS 2/3: 1-year PGCE, age 7-14 with specialisms in Maths, Science, English (60); 4-year BEd, age 7-14, with specialisms in Maths, Science, English, Music (48).

ITE Secondary: 1-year PGCE, age 11-18 (463) in Art, Classics, English, Geography, History, Maths, MFL, Music, Science (with Biology, Chemistry or Physics as a specialism), Drama, RE.

CPD / Higher Degrees: Advanced Diploma in Educational Studies; certificated and short courses for nursery, primary, secondary and special education teachers; 1-year f/t MPhil and 2-year p/t MEd allowing choice of taught or research programmes; f/t MPhil and PhD research degrees.

Other Courses: 3-year BA in Education Studies; development workshops through the Centre for Overseas & Developing Education (CODE) at Homerton College.

PARTNERSHIPS

The Faculty has strong ITE partnership arrangements with primary and secondary schools in East Anglia. It also has long experience of working collaboratively with schools and LEAs on CPD and on research and development initiatives. Research partnerships with secondary schools is the focus of current research.

MAIN RESEARCH AND DEVELOPMENT INTERESTS

*   School Effectiveness & Improvement
*   Classroom Teaching & Learning
*   Inclusion & Special Educational Needs
*   Professional Education & Learning
*   The History of Education
*   Mathematics Education
*   Language, Literacy & Literature
*   Citizenship, Gender & Social Justice
*   Information & Communication Technology

OTHER SPECIAL FEATURES

*   ESRC recognition for postgraduate educational research training.
*   Extensive library and computing facilities.

Canterbury Christ Church University College
CANTERBURY CT1 1QU

Tel: 01227 782236 / 782404
Fax: 01227 785761
Email: m.a.alfrey@cant.ac.uk
Website: www.cant.ac.uk

Contact Person: Mrs Margaret A Alfrey

Directions: Rail: From London Victoria take train to Canterbury East, then taxi to campus.

Staff:
Dean of Education:	Mrs Margaret Alfrey
Professors:	6
Other teaching staff:	67 f/t; 4 p/t
Research staff & students:	10

Overall FTE students in 1999/2000: 2116

COURSES

ITE Primary: 1-year PGCE, age 3-8/7-12 (125); 2-year p/t PGCE, age 3-8/7-12 (25); 3/4-year BA QTS, age 3-8/7-11 (254).
ITE KS 2/3: 1-year PGCE, age 7-14 (47) in Geography, Maths, RE, Science, English, Music, MFL.
ITE Secondary: 1-year PGCE (385) in Art, English, Geography, History, Maths, MFL, Music, RE, Science.
ITE Post-Compulsory: 1-year PGCE (60) in Business Administration, Sport Leisure & Tourism, Humanities & Social Sciences, Science, Maths & Technology, Health & Care; 2-year CertEd (650) with Bexhill College, Canterbury College, Lewisham College, Mid-Kent College, Orpington College, South Kent College, Thanet College; BA Professional Studies (PCET) (120); MA(Ed) The Learning Society (30).
CPD / Higher Degrees: Certificate; BA; Diploma; Masters and doctoral programmes; range of short courses for schools; school development days and other non-accredited consultancy work.

PARTNERSHIPS

All ITE courses operate in full partnership with schools in Kent or Medway and in some London Boroughs via the Urban Learning Foundation.

CPD Partnerships:
- Programmes for primary school consortia. Accredited and non-accredited, organised to meet needs identified at consortium headteacher meetings.
- Postgraduate Diploma/MA in School Improvement. School-based action research projects designed to meet development targets identified by the school.
- Kent Accreditation Partnership. Working with Kent LEA to broaden opportunities for accreditation for teachers.
- Bromley Accreditation Partnership. Working with Bromley LEA to offer joint programmes and to broaden opportunities for accreditation for teachers.

MAIN RESEARCH AND DEVELOPMENT INTERESTS

Research is provided and supported through the Education Research Committee and the Centre for Research in Education and all tutors are encouraged to involve themselves in research activity, supported by one of the following groupings:
- Early Childhood
- Primary Education
- Literacy
- Mathematics
- Special Educational Needs
- Teaching & Learning in Secondary Education
- Education Policy & Evaluation
- Teaching & Learning in Higher Education
- International English Language Education
- Education and Work Research Group (Attitudes to Work, Education & Training, Careers Education, Economics & Busines Education, Training for Trainers)
- Leadership & Management

OTHER SPECIAL FEATURES

- ESRC recognition for postgraduate educational reseach training.
- The College recruits students from abroad, particularly PGCE primary students from Canada.
- The College has strong links with a number of European institutions for student and staff exchange.
- The College runs a joint PGCE/Maîtrise in partnership with the Université du Littoral Côte Opale, Boulogne-Sur-Mer.
- The College's geographical location has been influential in the development of international links in the areas of research and teaching.

CARDIFF

Cardiff University
Division of Education
School of Social Sciences
21 Senghennydd Road
CARDIFF CF2 4YG

Tel: 01222 874533
Fax: 01222 874160
Email: swift@cf.ac.uk
Website: www.cf.ac.uk/uwcc/educt

Contact Person: Ms Jackie Swift, Administrator for Teaching & Learning

Directions: Road: M4 Exit Junction 32, A470, follow City Centre sign. University is signposted. Rail: Cardiff; 10 minutes by taxi, 20 minute walk.

Staff: Head of School: Professor Huw Beynon
Teaching staff: 23 f/t; 6 p/t
Research staff: 8

Overall FTE students in 1998/99: 490

COURSES

ITE Primary: BA Hons/BSc Economics: undergraduate programme in single or joint honours (combining education with another subject).
CPD / Higher Degrees: F/t or p/t modular MA; f/t or p/t MPhil; f/t or p/t PhD by research; EdD taught doctorate; 1-year PGCE (FE); 1-year Certificate in FE; 2-year p/t BEd Vocational Training; NPQH: Wales Assessment Centre and the Wales Training & Development Centre for the National Professional Qualification for Headteachers; short Inservice courses.

PARTNERSHIPS

The School has partnerships with FE colleges for the PGCE course, with LEAs and HEIs for the two NPQC Centres and with LEAs, Schools, HEIs and industry for the Learning Capital project.

MAIN RESEARCH AND DEVELOPMENT INTERESTS

Cardiff School of Education has adopted a strategy which focuses its research programme on the theme of the *Learning Society*. Accordingly, projects and other research activities aim to investigate processes of teaching and learning throughout the life-course, from early childhood through to adulthood. Whilst schools remain an extremely important element here, staff are also engaged in investigations of other educational settings, such as pre-school environments, further education colleges, universities and workplaces.

Internally, the Research Programme of the School is organised around three Research Groups:

- Education Management & Policy (EdMAP)
- Psychology of Education & SEN (PESEN)
- Education, Work & Employment (EWE)

All academic staff and research students are located within one of these groups which provide the immediate environment for each individual's research activities and give a good indication of topics for which applications are especially welcome. These include:

- EdMAP - the management of large-scale re-organisation of schools; new national policies on school inspection; national assessment procedures; professional socialisation of heads of subject departments in secondary schools; how processes internal to schools affect the underachievement of secondary-age boys.

- PESEN - pre-school education and later development; children's literacy; children with learning difficulties; shyness, social withdrawal, social confidence and creativity; transmitting language and culture to the next generation.

- EWE - the comparative analysis of national systems vocational education and training, participation and non-participation in education and training after leaving school; how employers organise training for multi-skilling in Britain and Germany; the governance of vocational education and training; the changing governance of the further education sector; graduate employment and student finance.

The School is currently developing a research network embracing schools, colleges and other educational and training institutions in Cardiff and its region, through its 'Learning Capital' Project.

University of Central England
Faculty of Education
Westbourne Road
Edgbaston
BIRMINGHAM   B15 3TN

Tel: 0121 331 6100 / 6063
Fax: 0121 331 6147
Email: diana.griffith@uce.ac.uk
Website: www.uce.ac.uk

Contact Person: Diana Griffith

Directions: To reach the Faculty from the City Centre, either take a taxi (10 minutes ride) or board a bus number 103, 10, 21, 22, 23 or 29 from Colmore Row by St Philip's Cathedral. If you arrive by train at Birmingham New Street, the bus numbers 21 and 29 load just beyond the station concourse by the Rotunda (by Bar St Martin's). Please ask for St George's Church, Westbourne Road. As you come into Westbourne Road you will see the buildings on your right. Car drivers should obtain route map from the Faculty in advance.

Staff: Acting Dean of Faculty: Alastair Pearce
              Teaching staff: 50 f/t

Overall FTE students in 1999/2000: 1500

COURSES

ITE Primary: 1-year PGCE, age 5-8 or 7-11 (40); 4-year BA Hons, age 3-8 or 7-11 (124 in year 1), students will choose 2 specialisms from Art, English, Geography, History, D&T.

ITE Secondary: 2-year shortened BEd Music (17 in year 1); PGCE Drama (20); PGCE Music (45)

CPD / Higher Degrees: Post-experience modular programme leading to Certificate in Professional Studies; Diploma in Professional Studies; Postgraduate Diploma; MA; research degrees leading to MPhil, PhD.

MAIN RESEARCH AND DEVELOPMENT INTERESTS

- Drama in Education
- Music Education
- Lifelong Learning
- Information Technology in Music
- Design & Technology in Education
- Computer-aided Learning
- Educational Use of the Internet
- Science Education
- Children's Understanding of Science
- Effective Science Teaching
- Environmental Education
- Successful Schools
- School Effectiveness & School Improvement
- Teaching & Learning
- Classroom Management & Organisation
- Management in Education
- Education Policy
- Early Years Education
- Appraisal
- Equal Opportunities in Education
- Special Educational Needs
- Language Studies
- Further Education
- Vocational Education & Training
- Post-16 Management & Quality Assurance
- Careers Guidance
- Mathematics Education
- Initial Teacher Education
- Mentoring
- European & International Studies in Education

Small bursaries may be available for teachers wishing to study in these areas.

OTHER SPECIAL FEATURES

- International Centre for Studies in Drama in Education
- Centre for Research into Primary Technology (CRIPT)
- Centre for Research into Music in Education (CRIME)

CHESTER

Chester College
School of Education
Parkgate Road
CHESTER   CH1 4BJ

Tel:	01244 392736
Fax:	01244 390585
Email:	d.lloyd@chester.ac.uk
Website:	www.chester.ac.uk

Contact Person: Mrs Elaine Barnes

Directions: The campus is situated at the junction of Cheyney Road and the A540 Parkgate Road, which is a continuation of Northgate Street leading out from the centre of the city. It is half a mile from the city walls and a 20 minute walk from the train station.

Staff: Dean of School: Mrs Elaine Barnes
             Teaching staff: 26 f/t; 25 p/t

Overall FTE students in 1999/2000: 735

COURSES

ITE Primary: 4-year BEd, age 3-11 with early years (3-8) or later years (7-11) specialism in English, Maths, Drama, Art, Geographical & Environmental Science, Theology & Religious Studies, PE; 1-year PGCE, age 5-11 (20).
ITE Secondary: 1-year PGCE, age 11-18 (70) in Maths, Art, Drama, MFL (French, German); PE, RE.
CPD / Higher Degrees: An extensive range of modular courses leading to certificate, diploma or degree awards; a range of short courses and tailored training days, run both on and off campus, can also lead to accreditation; MA Higher Education; MA Personal & Professional Development; Church Colleges Certificate.

PARTNERSHIPS

Chester has strong links with its three local LEAs: Cheshire, Wirral, Flintshire. It has partnership links with more than 300 primary schools and 30 secondary schools in these LEAs.

MAIN RESEARCH AND DEVELOPMENT INTERESTS

- Science Education
- Language & Literacy
- Special Educational Needs
- Arts & Drama Education
- Educational Use of the Internet
- Mentoring
- School Effectiveness
- Teaching & Learning in Primary Education
- The Teaching of Gifted Children

CHICHESTER

University College Chichester
Bishop Otter Campus
College Lane
CHICHESTER   PO19 4PE

Tel: 01243 816000
Fax: 01243 816080
Email: m.cremin@chihe.ac.uk
Website: www.chihe.ac.uk

Contact Person: Marlene Cremin, Faculty Administrative Officer

Directions: Road: *Chichester (Bishop Otter) Campus:* From Midhurst A286 to Chichester. From Portsmouth (west) or Brighton (east) A27 to Chichester, follow signs to City Centre, and University College Chichester. *Bognor Regis Campus:* From London A29 to Bognor Regis. From Portsmouth (west) or Brighton (east) A259 to Bognor Regis, follow signs to Hotham Park and University College Chichester.

Staff: Dean of Faculty: David Blake
              Teaching staff: 60 f/t

Overall FTE students in 1999/2000: 1475

COURSES

ITE Primary: 4-year BA QTS, age 3-8/5-8/7-11 (177) offered at University College Chichester and at the Crawley Centre, in association with Crawley College of Technology; 1-year PGCE, age 3-8/7-11 (59).
ITE KS 2/3: 4-year BA QTS, age 7-14 in Maths (10).
ITE Secondary: 1-year PGCE (93) in D&T, English, History, Maths, PE, RE; 2-year PGCE (10) in Maths; 4-year BA QTS (73) in PE, Maths; 2-year BA QTS (10) in Maths.
CPD / Higher Degrees: Certificate, Diploma and Master's level CPD Programme; various specialisms including Education Management, SEN, Mathematics Education, RE, ICT; short courses, conferences, consultancy programmes.
Other Courses: The Centre for International Education and Management (CIEM) offers a range of long award-bearing courses including the BEd (ELT), BEd (TESOL), Certificate and Diploma in Advanced Educational Studies (ELT Administration), MA (ELT) and MA in Education (International); in-

house and in-country short-course programmes and project management/consultancy.

PARTNERSHIPS

A range of partnerships, with 540 primary and secondary schools, LEAs (including Brighton & Hove, Poole, West Sussex, Greenwich, Hampshire, Isle of Wight, Portsmouth, Southampton), Ministries of Education (including Argentina, Hong Kong, Korea, Malaysia), several UK Higher Education Institutions (HEI) and overseas HEIs (in Malaysia, Japan, Korea, Madagascar, Portugal and the Seychelles). The College is in partnership with four LEAs (Hampshire, Kent, Surrey, West Sussex) and four HEIs (Brunel, Canterbury Christchurch, Roehampton, Greenwich) for NPQH training and assessment.

MAIN RESEARCH AND DEVELOPMENT INTERESTS

- Raising Achievement in Mathematics
- Children's experience of the National Curriculum in Physical Education
- Children's world-view project
- Excellence in Teaching
- Partnership in ITE
- Special Educational Needs in Schools
- The International Student Experience
- Provision of Written Feedback to Students on Taught MA Programmes
- Teachers' Attitudes to Primary Foreign Language Teaching
- Resource-based Data & Document Sets for the Applied Linguistics Curriculum
- Equal Opportunities in Education
- Teachers as Professionals
- The Impact of CPD on Professional Practice

DE MONTFORT

De Montfort University
School of Education
Polhill Avenue
BEDFORD   MK41 9EA

Tel: 01234 793124
Fax: 01234 217738
Email: pwalden@dmu.ac.uk
Website: www.dmu.ac.uk

Contact Person: Professor Peter Walden

Directions: *Lansdowne Road Campus:* From Bedford Town Centre follow A428 Bromham Road west, turn right at traffic lights into Union Street, Lansdowne Road is on the left. Reception is at No. 37. *Polhill Avenue Campus:* From Bedford Town Centre follow A428 Goldington Road east for 1 mile, campus is on left after traffic lights. *Centre for Postgraduate Teacher Education, Gateway House:* Gateway House is on City Campus, 15 minutes walk from Leicester main line station.

Staff: Head of School: Professor Peter Walden

No current information submitted for this edition. Please contact De Montfort University directly or refer to their website.

DERBY

University of Derby
School of Education & Social Science
Western Road
Mickleover
DERBY   DE3 5GX

Tel: 01332 622222
Fax: 01332 622746
Email: d.davies@derby.ac.uk
Website: www.derby.ac.uk/schools/ess

Contact Person: Professor David Davies, Dean of School

Directions: Road: From M1 Junction 25 take A52 towards Derby; follow sign A50 to Uttoxeter to Mickleover. From A38 Burton on Trent and A516 Uttoxeter follow signs for Mickleover. Rail: Derby (15 minutes by taxi). Bus: No. 15 or 16 from Bus Station, alight at Western Road/Chevin Avenue.

Staff: Dean of School: Professor David Davies
         Professors: 4
         Other teaching staff: 32 f/t; 5 p/t

Overall FTE students in 1999/2000: 360

COURSES

ITE Primary: 1-year PGCE, age 5-8/7-11 (20); 3-year BEd Hons, age 3-8/ 7-11 (67).
CPD / Higher Degrees: PG Certificate; PG Diploma; MEd, MPhil / PhD; extensive range of short courses/consultancy for schools.

PARTNERSHIPS

The School has partnerships for ITE with around 200 Primary schools in Derby, Derbyshire, East Staffordshire and West Nottinghamshire together with a Concordat with Derby City LEA and an agreement with Derbyshire to support and promote collaboration within both ITE and CPD. The School has extensive international links with Universities in Western and Eastern Europe, USA and CPD provision in Israel.

MAIN RESEARCH AND DEVELOPMENT INTERESTS

- Equal Opportunities - Equal Minorities
- Education Management
- Mathematical Education
- Technology & Information Technology
- European Awareness in Teacher Education / Inclusive Education in Europe
- Children's Rights & Social Justice
- Access & Widening Participation

DURHAM

University of Durham
School of Education
Leazes Road
DURHAM   DH1 1TA

Tel:	0191 374 1732
Fax:	0191 374 3506
Email:	d.m.galloway@durham.ac.uk
Website:	www.dur.ac.uk/~ded0www/

Contact Person: Professor David Galloway, Head of School

Directions: <u>Road:</u> Exit from A1(M) to A690, signposted Durham. At first roundabout continue on dual carriageway towards City Centre, under footbridge, take first left slip road into car park for School's main building and Reception. <u>British Rail:</u> Durham.

Staff: <u>Chair of the Board of Studies:</u> Professor David Galloway
<u>Professors:</u>   11
<u>Other teaching staff:</u> 50 f/t; 15 p/t
<u>Research staff:</u>   13

Overall FTE students in 1999/2000: 1145

COURSES

ITE Primary: 1-year PGCE, infant and junior phases (50); 3-year BA QTS, infant and junior phases (88); 2-year BSc in Science QTS, junior phase (30); 3-year BSc QTS in ICT, junior phase (24).

ITE Secondary: 1-year PGCE (271) in English, Drama, History, Geography, Music, Maths, Biology, Physics, Chemistry, MFL, RE, PE.

CPD / Higher Degrees: PhD; MA; MEd by research; EdD by taught course; MA/Advanced Diploma in Education; MA/Advanced Diploma in Counselling; specialist Certificates of Further Professional Studies.

Other Courses: BA Hons Sport in the Community; BA Hons Childhood & Arts; BA Hons Sport, Health & Exercise.

PARTNERSHIPS

Active, formal Partnerships exist with both Primary and Secondary schools throughout the North East region in support of our programmes of Initial Teacher Training. Schools are encouraged to participate in recruitment, training and course development. A highly successful STA course is run in association with the four Teesside Local Authorities and a good relationship with Durham LEA supports the development of our CPD and MA Modular programmes.

MAIN RESEARCH AND DEVELOPMENT INTERESTS

- The Arts & Education
- Assessment, Evaluation & School Effectiveness
- Counselling & Education
- Environmental Understanding & Education
- Lifelong Learning
- Physical Education & Sport
- Philosophical and Critical Approaches to Education
- Science & Maths Education

OTHER SPECIAL FEATURES

The School of Education has established partnerships in Germany, France, Spain, Kenya, Hong Kong and Singapore and working contacts with the USA, Canada, Australia, New Zealand, Sweden, Greece, Argentina, Qatar and Slovenia. Our Curriculum, Evaluation & Management (CEM) Centre is a leading provider of indicator systems for every level of Primary and Secondary Education.

EAST ANGLIA

University of East Anglia
School of Education & Professional Development
University Plain
NORWICH   NR4 7TJ

Tel: 01603 592856
Fax: 01603 593446
Email: edu.info@uea.ac.uk
Website: www.uea.ac.uk

Contact Person: Ms Debbie Green, School Clerk

Directions: Road: From Norwich Southern Ring-Road (A47) take B1108 towards Norwich and follow signs to University. Rail: Norwich; 15 minutes by taxi.

Staff: Dean of School: Professor Nigel Norris
             Teaching staff: 27 f/t; 7 p/t
             Research staff: 7

Overall FTE students in 1999/2000: 550

COURSES

ITE Primary: 1-year PGCE (150)
ITE Secondary: 1-year PGCE (173) in English, Maths, History, Geography, Science (Chemistry, Physics, Biology), RE, MFL.
CPD / Higher Degrees: A wide range of advanced award bearing courses aimed at teachers and other professional groups; p/t Advanced Certificate; Postgraduate Diploma; Advanced Diploma; MA courses by credit accumulation; MA courses; f/t and p/t research degrees; MEd; MPhil; PhD; EdD.
Other Courses: 1-year f/t Diploma in Counselling; 2-year p/t MA in Counselling Studies; Egyptian Ministry of Education 12-week courses for subject specialists and head teachers; TTA bridging courses RE.

PARTNERSHIPS

Joint School/UEA partnerships for both Primary and Secondary PGCE programmes. Liaison with Norfolk and Suffolk LEAs over CPD provision. Norwich Area Schools Consortium (TTA funded) research project.

42

MAIN RESEARCH AND DEVELOPMENT INTERESTS

- Programme & Policy Evaluation
- Teacher Development & Action Research
- Schooling & Curriculum Studies
- Youth Theory Method & Knowledge Production
- Education & Training in the Professions
- Qualitative Approaches to Educational Enquiry

OTHER SPECIAL FEATURES

The School of Education & Professional Development has a number of specialist teaching and research centres including

- Centre for Applied Research in Education (CARE)
- Centre for Applied Research in Visual Arts Education
- Centre for Counselling Studies
- Centre for Research & Development in Religious Education

The School has strong cross-professional and multi-disciplinary links with other UEA Schools. In conjunction with the UEA Staff Training and Development Office, the School offers awards in Higher Education Practice for academic staff.

University of East London
Department of Education & Community Studies
Longbridge Road
DAGENHAM   RM8 2AS

Tel: 0181 849 3509
Fax: 0181 849 3582
Email: t.ohaire@uel.ac.uk
Website: www.uel.ac.uk

Contact Person: Trevor O'Haire, Departmental Administrator

Directions: District Line or British Rail to Barking Station, then 87 bus to campus (10 minutes). Map available on request.

Staff: Head of School: Mr Jim Graham
Professors: 1
Other teaching staff: 17 f/t; 10 p/t
Research staff: 5

Overall FTE students in 1999/2000: 425

COURSES

ITE Primary: 1-year PGCE, nursery and all primary age groups (137, including 25 places for ICT specialism and 10 places for advanced Early Years).
CPD / Higher Degrees: The following degrees are offered in conjunction with the Centre for Institutional Studies and the Department of Educational Development Services: MA Primary Education Practice; MA Professional Practice in Education; MA Learning & Teaching in HE; MA Voluntary Sector Studies; MA Public & Community Service; MA/MSc by Independent Study; MA by Work-based Learning; EdD (awaiting validation); MPhil; PhD.
Other Courses: Undergraduate Degree Scheme - Students may combine f/t or p/t studies of Education with National Curriculum Subjects in order to teach in schools, or combine other subjects to pursue careers outside school teaching. The following degrees are offered: BA Education & Community Studies; BSc ICT in Education (without QTS for intending Primary Teachers continuing to PGCE); BSc New Technology & Education; BA South Asian Studies (awaiting validation); BA Early Childhood (awaiting validation); BA Language & Education (awaiting validation); DipHE Playwork & Youth Studies (in partnership with Thurrock College).

PARTNERSHIPS

ITT & CPD partnerships with the London Boroughs of Newham, Barking & Dagenham, Redbridge, Havering, Tower Hamlets, Waltham Forest, Hackney.

MAIN RESEARCH AND DEVELOPMENT INTERESTS

East London Assessment Group - specialises in the design and standardisation of tests in education and holds contracts with QCA and several publishers for development and evaluation.

Centre for Institutional Studies - specialises in research in Post-Compulsory education and voluntary sector development, holding contracts for evaluation on City Challenge, evaluation and volunteering.

Education Development Research Network - specialises in research in teaching and learning in HE.

Other staff research interests include:

- Partnership in Teacher Education
- Teacher Professionalism
- Refugees Education
- Bilingualism
- South Asian Culture & Education
- Supplementary Schooling
- Quality Assurance Systems in HE & Teacher Education

OTHER SPECIAL FEATURES

The University is a multiethnic community which celebrates diversity and has particular course emphases on equal opportunities in the urban environment. We provide ladders of opportunities from Access courses or teaching assistant courses through a range of degree programmes in Education and related professional areas, to Qualified Teacher Status and onwards to post-experience and postgraduate qualifications. Many programmes are offered in partnership with LEAs, outposted in teacher's centres with contributions from expert practitioners. We welcome overseas students and offer individually tailored support packages.

EDGE HILL

Edge Hill University College
School of Education
St Helens Road
ORMSKIRK L39 4QP

Tel: 01695 584326
Fax: 01695 570835
Email: bridgf@staff.ehche.ac.uk
Website: www.ehche.ac.uk

Contact Person: Mrs Freda Bridge, Head of School

Directions: Road: M6 Junction 26, M58 Junction 3, A570 (Southport)

Staff: Head of School: Mrs Freda Bridge
Teaching staff: 35 f/t
(with significant contributions from staff in other Schools of the Institution)

Overall FTE students in 1999/2000: 1500

COURSES

ITE Primary: 1-year PGCE, age 3-8/7-11; 3-year BA QTS, age 3-8/7-11 in Maths, English, Science, History, PE, Art, Music; RE.
ITE KS 2/3: 3-year BA QTS in English; 3-year BSc QTS in D&T, IT.
ITE Secondary: 1-year PGCE, age 11-18 in Maths, English, Science, MFL (French, German, Spanish, Urdu), D&T, History, Geography, Music, PE; 1-year PGCE, age 14-19 in Business Education; 2-year BSc QTS (part 2) in D&T, Maths, Science, Business Education; 3-year BSc QTS, age 11-18 in D&T, Maths, Science.
CPD / Higher Degrees: Postgraduate Programme leading to Postgraduate Certificate/Postgraduate Diploma/MA with specialist pathways in Early Years Education, Education Management, Educational Studies, Mathematics Education, Mentoring, Primary Education, Special Educational Needs, SEN Coordination (to PGD level).
Professional Programme leading to Certificate of Professional Development with modules in Primary Curriculum, Language and Literacy, Early Years, Leadership and Management, ICT, Management of Pupil Behaviour, School Improvement, SEN.

Other Courses: Education Studies within the Institution's Modular Programme; BA in Education and Literacy (p/t degree course); Early Childhood Studies.

MAIN RESEARCH AND DEVELOPMENT INTERESTS

- Special Educational Needs
- Teaching and Learning in Higher Education
- Mentoring
- Teaching as a Profession
- Multiple Intelligence Theory
- Phonological Awareness and Metacognition
- School Effectiveness
- Literacy
- PSE / Citizenship
- Early Years Education
- Primary Curriculum
- History
- Geography
- School-based Teacher Training
- Student Learning
- Newly Qualified Teachers
- Education Management
- Children's Rights in Education

EXETER

University of Exeter
School of Education
Heavitree Road
EXETER   EX1 2LU

Tel: 01392 264959
Fax: 01392 264922
Email: s.m.thomas@exeter.ac.uk
Website: www.ex.ac.uk/education

Contact Person: Sue M Thomas, Head of Administration

Directions: Road: M5 from Bristol, exit at Junction 30, follow directions into city centre to Heavitree Road. Campus is opposite police station. Main car park on Magdalen Road. Rail: Exeter St David's (Paddington Line) or Exeter Central (Waterloo Line); 10/15 minutes by taxi. Frequent minibus service.

Staff: Head of School: Professor Robert Burden
             Professors: 10
             Other teaching staff: 28 f/t; 17p/t
             Research staff & students: 190

Overall FTE students in 1999/2000: 1350

COURSES

ITE Primary: 4-year BA(Ed) (35) in Maths, Science; PGCE (135) in Early Years, English, Humanities, Maths, Music, Science.
ITE KS 2/3: PGCE (30) in D&T, English/Literacy.
ITE Secondary: 4-year BSc(Ed) (30) in Maths or Science; 2-year BA(Ed) (15) in D&T, Maths or Science; PGCE (417) in Art, D&T, English, Geography, History, Maths, MFL, PE, RE, Science.
CPD / Higher Degrees: MEd (Educational Psychology); BPhil(Ed)/MEd; EdD; PhD; MPhil; extensive range of modular p/t courses.
Other Courses: Inservice short courses offered in the South West Region, nationally and internationally. Certificates in Advanced Professional Studies in Education. National and international conferences.

PARTNERSHIPS

Partnership agreements for ITT signed with over 300 schools across South West England and in London, Birmingham and Ontario, Canada.

MAIN RESEARCH AND DEVELOPMENT INTERESTS

- Arts Education
- Curriculum Innovation & Evaluation
- Early Childhood Education
- Educational Psychology
- Education Management & Leadership
- English Education
- Geography Education
- History Education
- Knowledge & Learning in Transition into Adulthood
- Literacy & Language
- Mathematics Education
- Music Education
- Post-16 Education: Learning Careers
- Physical Education
- Religious Education
- Science Education
- Social Moral, Spiritual & Cultural Education
- Special Educational Needs
- Telematics & New Technology in Education
- Teaching & Teacher Education
- Teaching English as a Foreign Language (TEFL)

GLAMORGAN

University of Glamorgan
The Business School
PONTYPRIDD CF37 1DL

Tel: 01443 482352
Fax: 01443 482989
Email: cjames1@glam.ac.uk
Website: www.glam.ac.uk

Contact Person: Professor Chris James

Directions: Nearest rail station: Treforest, three minutes walk from the university.

Staff:	Head of School:	Professor Chris James
	Professors:	2
	Other teaching staff:	6 f/t; 6p/t
	Research staff & students:	3

Overall FTE students in 1999/2000: 45

COURSES

CPD / Higher Degrees: MSc in Educational Management; MA in Professional Development in Education
Other Courses: MSc in Communicating Science; MA in Professional Development in Educational Policy and Strategic Management; MA in Educational Development.

PARTNERSHIPS

With
* Techniquest in Cardiff for the MSc in Communicating Science
* SEO Wales for the MA in Professional Development in Educational Policy and Strategic Management
* the Bridgend, Caerphilly, Merthyr Tydfil and Rhondda-CynonTaf LEAs in school improvement research.

MAIN RESEARCH AND DEVELOPMENT INTERESTS

- Educational Leadership
- Management & Policy
- Organisational Learning
- Management Learning
- Higher Education Policy & Practice

GREENWICH

University of Greenwich

I. School of Education
   Avery Hill Campus
   Bexley Road
   ELTHAM SE9 2PQ

II. School of PCET
   Maritime Campus
   Park Row, Greenwich
   LONDON SE10 G25

Tel: 0800 005006
Fax: 0181 331 8145
Email: m.stiasny@gre.ac.uk (Education)
           i.mcnay@gre.ac.uk (PCET)
Website: www.gre.ac.uk

Contact Person: Dr Mary Stiasny, Head of School of Education
                    Professor Ian McNay, Head of School of PCET

Directions: Eltham (Education), Greenwich or Maze Hill Stations (PCET).

Staff: <u>Head of School:</u>   Dr Mary Stiasny (Education)
                                Professor Ian McNay (PCET)
         <u>Teaching staff:</u>   35 f/t Education; 24 f/t PCET
         <u>Research staff:</u>   5 (PCET)

Overall FTE students in 1999/2000: 2000

COURSES

ITE Primary: 4-year BA/BSc Hons QTS in English, Maths, Science, D&T (40); 3-year BEd (45); 1-year PGCE (52).
ITE KS 2/3: 4-year BA Hons QTS in D&T (30).
ITE Secondary: 3-year BA Hons QTS in PE, D&T (70); 1-year PGCE in Art, PE, D&T (32).
ITE Post-Compulsory: CertEd/PGCE (PCET) (350); Postgraduate Diploma (HE) (40); Certificate in Teaching Competence (PCET); Certificate in Teaching Competence (Learning Support) (10) - these match FENTO standards.
CPD / Higher Degrees: MA; MSc; PG Dip; BEd Hons; BA Hons; BSc Hons; DPSE; CPSE; PGDip HE (recognised by ENB and expected to satisfy requirements of the Institute of Learning & Teaching in HE; PGCE FE; Certificate in Teaching Competencies (FE); PCET teaches some units via computer mediated communication; CertEd/PGCE (PCET), PGDip(HE) available through flexible and distance learning; PhD and Masters degrees by research available; individual units can be studied under the Associate Student Programmes.

Other Courses: Licensed Teacher Programme; 20-day courses in Maths, Science, Geography, History, Technology; Early Years short courses; short courses in Education Management and other topics; D-series for NVQ assessors.

PARTNERSHIPS

The School of Education has very strong partnerships with schools and LEAs, with School Partnerships forming the basis of Primary and Secondary ITE. CPD is developed by partnerships with schools and LEAs. These partnerships and consortia provide both higher degrees and accredited INSET programmes for practising teachers.

The School of PCET builds its activities around a set of partnerships: on the pre-service courses a core of 16 partner colleges provide placement experience and tuition support for groups of up to 20 students; the inservice qualification - CertEd, PGCE - are offered both by the School and, through franchising, by over 20 colleges in a UK network; the BA/BSc has a smaller network of four. Joint research activities are now developing with partner colleges. There are partner colleges in other countries for a range of European projects.

MAIN RESEARCH AND DEVELOPMENT INTERESTS

- Design & Technology Education
- Vocational Curriculum
- Education Management
- Intercultural Education
- Mentoring
- Special Needs
- Partnership between HE and Schools and FE Colleges
- Equity & Diversity
- Policy Analysis
- Career Progression & Change in Education Professionals
- Impact of CMC on Education Processes

OTHER SPECIAL FEATURES

The School of Education and the School of PCET have an extensive range of accreditation partnerships with LEAs, School and Colleges to assist in the professional development of teachers and lecturers. Accreditation for prior and experiential learning is available. There is also a strong involvement in European activities including student exchanges with partner institutions.

HERTFORDSHIRE

University of Hertfordshire
Department of Education
Watford Campus
Aldenham
WATFORD   WD2 8AT

Tel: 01707 284000
Fax: 01707 285626
Email: c.d.cook@herts.ac.uk
Website: www.herts.ac.uk

Contact Person: Professor Chris Cook

Directions: Road: Exit from M1 (Junction 5), follow A41 towards Harrow, turn left at roundabout towards Aldenham, fork left into Aldenham Village. Campus drive is opposite Aldenham church. Rail: Watford Junction or Radlett; 10 minutes by taxi or 13 minutes by University*bus*.

Staff: Head of Department: Professor Chris Cook
          Professors: 3
          Other teaching staff: 45 f/t; 25 p/t
          Research staff & students: 30

Overall FTE students in 1999/2000: 850

COURSES

ITE Primary: 1-year PGCE (110) with KS2, KS1 and Nursery pathways; 4-year BEd Hons (140) in Art, Early Years, English, Geography, Science, Maths, Religious Studies, SEN; 2-year BEd for students with overseas qualifications enabling them to qualify as teachers (10).

ITE Secondary: 1-year PGCE (82) in Maths, Science, English, MFL, Art, Geography.

ITE Post-Compulsory: 2-year p/t CertEd/PGCE (Post-Compulsory Education & Training) (90).

CPD / Higher Degrees: F/t or p/t modular INSET programme leading to awards from University Certificate to MA/MEd; 2-year p/t Postgraduate Diploma (Education of the Hearing Impaired); MPhil/PhD.

Other Courses: Registered and Graduate Teacher programmes; 4-year p/t BA Early Childhood Studies; Specialist Teacher's Assistant course; Distance Learning course leading to University Certificate in Early Childhood Education & Care; 1/2 year BA/BEd courses for international students; extensive programme of short courses, conferences and seminars for schools, teachers and others in the education and care sector; national and international educational consultancy.

PARTNERSHIPS

The University has partnership arrangements with over 500 primary and 50 secondary schools in ten LEAs. Partner schools offer ITE placements and selected teachers act as teacher tutors to campus-based courses. The TTA funded CPD programme involves partnerships with LEAs in managing and delivering courses. Some of the CPD programme is taught in partner schools.

MAIN RESEARCH AND DEVELOPMENT INTERESTS

- Literacy, Numeracy & Science in Primary Schools
- Early Childhood Education & Care
- Special Educational Needs (especially hearing impairment and autism and associated syndromes)
- Equality Issues in Education
- Subject Teaching in Primary Schools
- Education & Teacher Education in Developing Countries

HUDDERSFIELD

University of Huddersfield
School of Education & Professional Development
Holly Bank Campus
Holly Bank Road, Lindley
HUDDERSFIELD   HD3 3BP

Tel: 01484 478249
Fax: 01484 514784
Email: education@hud.ac.uk
Website: www.hud.ac.uk

Contact Person: Course Enquiry Line - 0870 901 5555

Directions: Road: Exit from M62; follow signs towards Huddersfield; after first set of traffic lights turn right onto Holly Bank Road. The campus is on the right. Rail: Huddersfield; 5 minutes by taxi or frequent bus service.

Staff: Dean of School: Geoff Calderbank
            Professors: 3
            Teaching staff: 35 f/t; 40 p/t
            Research staff & students: 20

Overall FTE students in 1999/2000:   1414

COURSES

ITE KS 2/3:   1-year PGCE, age 7-14 (18) in D&T. Other subjects under consideration.

ITE Secondary: F/t 1- or 2-year PGCE; f/t 2-year BEd/BEd Hons (197) in D&T, Business Studies, IT, Maths, Science, Music.

ITE Post-Compulsory: F/t and p/t courses offered at Huddersfield and other centres for PGCE (FE) and CertEd (FE).

CPD / Higher Degrees: Postgraduate Diploma, MEd, MA (Professional Development), EdD; MPhil and PhD degrees by research; short courses for school teachers mainly following TTA priorities; CertEd/MEd/MPhil/PhD courses for teachers from overseas.

Other Courses: BA Education & Training; BA (Community Studies); Graduate and Registered Teacher Schemes with p/t access route (primary and secondary).

56

PARTNERSHIPS

For school-teacher training, the University works closely in partnership with some 80 schools within a 35 mile radius of Huddersfield. Placements are made close to students' homes where possible. In FE the University works with some 32 franchise centres in the North and North East for deliverery of initial and inservice training.

MAIN RESEARCH AND DEVELOPMENT INTERESTS

- Technical and Vocational education both in the UK and overseas
- ICT in Education
- Management of change
- Concept Development
- Youth & Community Education

OTHER SPECIAL FEATURES

The School has a particular focus on Information Technology in its own right and as ICT across the curriculum.

The School has a tradition of including mature students and those from ethnic minorities in its student body.

HULL

University of Hull
Institute for Learning
Cottingham Road
HULL   HU6 7RX

Tel: 01482 465406
Fax: 01482 466133
Email: t.d.cuthbertson@pdt.hull.ac.uk
Website: www.hull.ac.uk

Contact Person: Mr Ian Marriott, Administrator, CPDTE

Directions: Road: At the end of the M62 continue along the A63 to the first set of traffic lights. Continue for a further 2.4 miles and exit at signs for A15 Humber Bridge and A164 Beverley. Follow signs for Beverley until you reach the turn off for Cottingham. The University is signposted from Cottingham Village. Rail: Hull Paragon Station; 20 minutes by taxi.

Staff: Director of Centre: Professor Graham Chesters
             Professors: 2
             Other teaching staff: 26 f/t; 7 p/t
             Research staff & students: 77

Overall FTE students in 1999/2000: 370

COURSES

ITE Primary: 1-year PGCE, age 7-11 (47)
ITE Secondary: 1-year PGCE (153) in Economics, English, Geography, History, Maths, MFL, RE, Science (Biology, Chemistry, Physics); 4-year BSc Integrated Hons QTS in Biology or Chemistry with Education (annual intake of 11).
CPD / Higher Degrees: 1-year f/t and modular p/t programmes leading to Advanced Certificates, Advanced Diplomas and Masters degrees; f/t and p/t research degrees; MEd; MPhil; EdD; PhD; short courses for schools.
Other Courses: P/t transitional MA in European Education.

PARTNERSHIPS

The Centre for Professional Development and Training in Education has developed partnerships with 46 primary and 47 secondary schools in the delivery of its ITE programmes. These schools are distributed throughout the City of Hull, the East Riding of Yorkshire, the North Riding of Yorkshire, North

Lincolnshire and Northeast Lincolnshire. The Centre also collaborates with the Hull Education Department in the delivery of its Special Needs programmes.

MAIN RESEARCH AND DEVELOPMENT INTERESTS

- Argumentation in Schools & Higher Education
- Visual Literacy
- Language Education & Arts Education
- The Philosophy & Psychology of Values Education
- The Management of the Primary Sector in the Education
- Policy Making in Education
- Science Teaching
- The Primary School Curriculum
- Children's Physical Activity & Grounded Theory
- Education in Developing Countries
- Mathematics Education
- Cardiac Adaptation to Exercise
- Special Educational Needs
- Teacher Effectiveness
- Health Education & Health-based Physical Education in Primary and Secondary Schools
- Research Methods in Education
- Primary Education with Particular Reference to the Infant Stage
- Primary Science Education
- Educational Technology & Media Studies
- Curriculum Studies
- Further & Higher Education
- Teaching & Training
- Assessment in English
- Telematics in Education

OTHER SPECIAL FEATURES

The Institute for Learning runs a distance-taught PhD programme in Hong Kong. It validates an Advanced Diploma programme running at the Christian Leadership in Education Office (CLEO), Cork, Eire. CLEO also assists in the running of distance-taught MEd and PhD degrees in that part of Ireland. The Institute also validates education programmes running at Doncaster College and North Lindsey College, Scunthorpe.

The Centre for Educational Studies is also responsible for a BSc degree in PE and Sports Science.

KEELE

Keele University
Department of Education
KEELE ST5 5BG

Tel: 01782 583114
Fax: 01782 583555
Email: eda40@keele.ac.uk
Website: www.keele.ac.uk/depts/ed/educ2.htm

Contact Person: Departmental Co-ordinator

Directions: Road: Exit J15 from M6, A519 to Newcastle-under-Lyme. Campus on A525, 2 miles west of Newcastle. Department based in Chancellor's Building. Rail: Stoke-on-Trent, 15 minutes by taxi; Crewe, 20 minutes by taxi.

Staff:
Head of Department:	Professor Jenny Ozga	
Professors:	5	
Other teaching staff:	20 f/t; 2 p/t	
Research staff & students:	8	

Overall FTE students in 1999/2000: 445

COURSES

ITE Primary: 1-year PGCE, age 7-11 (25); 4-year Concurrent Certificate in Primary Education, age 7-11 (14), offered in a 'package' with an undergraduate 'joint honours degree' in Conductive Education and Psychology.

ITE Secondary: 1-year PGCE, age 11-18 (300) in Biology, Chemistry, English, French, Geography, Geology, German, History, IT, Maths, MFL, Physics, Social Sciences; 2-year PGCE Maths Conversion Course (12); 2-year Science PGCE (16); 2-year IT (12); PGCE FE course, f/t and p/t (35/30)

CPD / Higher Degrees: Short courses and consultancies are offered in schools, colleges and various centres in the region, as well as in the Department; a range of taught Higher Degree courses including MBA/DpBA (Education), MA/PG Diploma in Education Management and the MA/PG Diploma in Educational Improvement and Effectiveness. Courses are modular and can be taken e.g. MA p/t (from 2 years); Research degrees (MPhil, PhD) may also be taken f/t or p/t.

Other Courses: Educational Studies: 3-year (68) subject offered within Keele's dual honours degree programme; must be taken in combination with another subject. This course seeks to prepare students for a range of professional careers involving - or loosely allied to - education and training.

PARTNERSHIPS

The Keele school/college partnerships are well established on the Secondary, FE and Primary PGCE Courses in Cheshire Staffordshire, Stoke-on-Trent, Shropshire and Wolverhampton. CPD and departmental research links include a wide constituency of LEAs and other national and international organisations i.e. DfEE, NCET, SCAA, Peto Institute in Hungary, SCOPE.

MAIN RESEARCH AND DEVELOPMENT INTERESTS

The Keele Department has two principal areas of research activity:
- Teacher Professionalism
- Effective Education

The first area brings together work on a range of issues from mentoring in initial training to professional development in specific subjects and teachers' development needs in Information and Communications Technology. In addition, researchers engage with frameworks for exploring current and recent changes in teachers' work and the consequences for teachers' professional status and identity. Research on Effective Education is led by the Keele Centre for Successful Schools (KCSS) and includes work on pupil and teacher attitudes, management effectiveness and professional development needs. The Department has a strong research presence in policy issues in education, including education-economy links, and is a partner in several major EU funded projects with policy implications for teachers and schools.

OTHER SPECIAL FEATURES

A distinctive feature of the Department is its concern to use research, consultancy and teaching to support effective education in the local, national and international contexts. Activity contributing to this broad aim is very wide-ranging and includes the training of conductors in association with the Peto Institute, partnership-based research projects, on among other things, bullying, mentoring and ICT and the new EdD for policy-makers and administrators.

Keele Improving Schools Network (KIS*Net*) has been established to help schools keep up with the latest research and to disseminate and share good practice.

KING ALFRED'S

**King Alfred's College of Higher Education
School of Education
WINCHESTER   SO22 4NR**

Tel: 01962 827381
Fax: 01962 827479
Email: anne.william@wkac.ac.uk
Website: www.wkac.ac.uk

Contact Person: Professor Anne Williams, Head of School

Directions: <u>Rail:</u> Winchester Station; then either taxi or 10 minute walk to campus.

Staff: <u>Head of School:</u>   Professor Anne Williams
           <u>Teaching staff:</u>   32 f/t; 3 p/t
           <u>Research staff:</u>   2

Overall FTE students in 1999/2000: 1030

COURSES

ITE Primary: 1-year PGCE, age 5-11 (40); 4-year Primary BA Hons, age 3-8 and 7-11 with one Special Subject from: Art & Design, D&T, Drama, English, Geography, History, Mathematics, Music, Physical Education, Religious Studies, Science, Advanced Early Years.
CPD / Higher Degrees: Modular Post-Graduate Programme of Continuing Professional Development. This programme offers qualified teachers and educationalists a wide variety of opportunities to develop their professional skills and carry out enquiries into their own practice. Modules of study include a wide variety of Professional Modules and Compulsory Modules specific to the MA programme. The programme is modular and flexible enabling credits to be accumulated, with studies and assignments differentiated to cater for the different needs and levels of professional qualification being sought.
Other Courses: Education Studies (non-QTS) on the Combined Honours Programme.

PARTNERSHIPS

The College works in partnership with schools and LEAs in ITE and CPD and also with a range of organisations in the development of international projects.

MAIN RESEARCH AND DEVELOPMENT INTERESTS

A practitioner research group, a social relations research group and an international education group form the main focus for research activity.

KINGSTON

Kingston University
School of Education
Kingston Hill
KINGSTON-UPON-THAMES   KT2 7LB

Tel: 0181 547 2000
Fax: 0181 547 7116
Email:
Website: http://polaris.king.ac.uk:8080/

Contact Person:

Directions: Road: Leave A3 at Robin Hood Roundabout and proceed towards Kingston along Kingston Vale/Kingston Hill. The University's Kingston Hill Centre is on the left hand side of the road about three-quarters of a mile from the roundabout. Rail: Kingston (3 miles) and Norbiton (2 miles). From Kingston take no. 85 bus or taxi to Centre.

Staff: Head of School: Mrs Mary Bousted

No current information submitted for this edition. Please contact Kingston University directly or refer to their website.

LANCASTER

Lancaster University
Department of Educational Research
Cartmel College
LANCASTER   LA1 4YL

Tel:	01524 594083
Fax:	01524 592914
Email:	s.horne@lancaster.ac.uk
Website:	www.lancs.ac.uk

Contact Person: Sheena Horne

Directions: Road: Leave the M6 at Junction 33 and take the A6 north towards Lancaster. The University Campus is on the right after about one and a half miles. Turn right at the traffic lights and follow the main drive to the roundabout. Take the first exit and follow the perimeter road until you reach County Avenue. The Department is on C floor of Cartmel College. Rail: Lancaster; 15 minutes by taxi.

Staff: Head of Department: Dr Murray Saunders
Teaching staff: 14
Research staff: 12

Overall FTE students in 1999/2000: 175

COURSES

CPD / Higher Degrees: F/t and p/t MA/Diploma in Education with specialist schemes (e.g. Women's Studies & Education, Physics & Education; p/t MSc/Diploma in IT & Learning (distance learning option); f/t and p/t MPhil and PhD by research; p/t MPhil/PhD in Educational Research, taught element, aimed at experienced professionals in HE and FE.

Other Courses: BA Hons Educational Studies; BA Hons Educational Research; Combined major degree courses: BA Hons Educational Studies & Applied Social Science, BA Hons Educational Studies & History, BA Hons Criminology & Educational Studies, BA Hons Educational Studies & Psychology, BA Hons Educational Studies & RE, BA Hons Educational Studies & Sociology.

MAIN RESEARCH AND DEVELOPMENT INTERESTS

Research centres within the Department:
- Centre for the Study of Education & Training (CSET)
- Centre for Studies in Advanced Learning Technology (CSALT)
- Community Access Programme (CAP)

Areas of research:
- Post-compulsory Education & Training
- Psychology of Teaching & Learning
- Gender Studies
- Advanced Learning Technology
- Policy & Organisation

The Department also has special expertise in qualitative methodologies in research and evaluation.

University of Leeds
School of Education
LEEDS   LS2 9JT

Tel: 0113 233 4545
Fax: 0113 233 4541
Email: a.w.moore@education.leeds.ac.uk
Website: www.education.leeds.ac.uk

Contact Person: Ms Alison Moore

Directions: Road: From City Centre or Inner Ring Road follow local sign direction to University. Enter University precinct by main entrance beside the Parkinson Building. British Rail: Leeds City Station (less than 1 mile). Buses every few minutes (nos. 93 and 96).

Staff: Head of School: Dr Paul Sharp
            Professors: 7
            Other teaching staff: 50 f/t; 10 p/t
            Research staff: 19

Overall FTE students in 1999/2000: 900

COURSES

ITE Primary: 1-year PGCE, age 3-8; 5-8/7-11
ITE Secondary: 1-year PGCE (450) in Biology, Chemistry, Physics, English, French, German, Spanish, Geography, History, IT, D&T, Maths, Music, RE, Social Science.
CPD / Higher Degrees: Certificates; Advanced and Postgraduate Diplomas; MEd; MEd by research; MPhil; EdD; PhD; specialist programmes exist for institutional and professional development: School Management & Leadership, Primary & Secondary Curriculum Leadership, SEN, Deaf Education, Severe Learning Difficulties, Primary Education, TESOL, ICT, School Curriculum areas.
Other Courses: International Education: Custom-built short courses and attachments for overseas students; specialist post-graduate Diploma/MEd options and Doctoral studies in a wide range of areas. Some courses are being developed for teaching at a distance, including the new Access Certificate in TESOL, MEd in TESOL, Advanced Diploma in Deaf Education and MEd in IT, Multimedia and Education.

PARTNERSHIPS

ITE: Formal partnerships exist with 69 secondary and 32 primary schools.
CPD: There is a long history of collaboration and co-development with teachers, schools and LEAs, directly and through the North and West Yorkshire PDC, in award and non-award bearing courses.

MAIN RESEARCH AND DEVELOPMENT INTERESTS

- Arts and humanities education
- Computer-based learning
- Learning systems design
- Special educational needs
- Motor control, development and impairment
- Learning difficulties
- Emotional and behavioural difficulties
- Deaf education and deaf studies
- Language education
- Language teacher education
- Post-14 education and training
- Sociology of education, training and youth
- Further and higher education
- Work-place learning
- Policy analysis and evaluation
- Primary and pre-school education
- Assessment
- Primary curriculum
- Research in development education
- Educational psychology
- Teacher education and professional learning
- Historical and policy studies in science education
- Learning in science
- Mathematics education

OTHER SPECIAL FEATURES

- Assessment and Evaluation Unit
- Centre for Studies in Science and Mathematics Education
- Centre for Policy Studies in Education
- Learning in Science Research Group
- 14-19 Research Group

LEEDS METROPOLITAN

Leeds Metropolitan University
Faculty of Cultural & Education Studies
Beckett Park Campus
LEEDS   LS6 3QS

School of Teaching & Education Studies:
Tel: 0113 283 3169
Fax: 0113 283 7410
Email: w.nuttall@lmu.ac.uk
Website: www.lmu.ac.uk
Contact Person: Ms Emma Toon
Staff: Head of School: Ms Wendy Nuttall
            Teaching staff: 32 f/t; 4 p/t
            Research staff: 2

School of Professional Education & Development:
Tel: 0113 283 7414
Fax: 0113 283 3181
Email: g.holmes@lmu.ac.uk
Website: www.lmu.ac.uk
Contact Person: Joyce Tate
Staff: Head of School: Professor Gary Holmes
            Teaching staff: 19 f/t; 10 p/t
            Research staff: 2

Overall FTE students in 1999/2000: 900

Directions: Beckett Park Campus is situated in Headingly, off Otley Road (A660). Entrances to Beckett Park are from Churchwood Avenue and St Chad's Drive.

COURSES

ITE Primary: BA Hons QTS Early Childhood Education; BEd Hons Primary Education; PGCE Early Years.
ITE KS 2/3:   BA Hons in D&T, Maths, IT.
ITE Secondary: BA Hons QTS in D&T, IT, PE; PGCE in PE.
CPD / Higher Degrees: MA Childhood Studies; MA PE; Leeds Inservice Accreditation Scheme (LISAS); MA Professional Studies; MSc in Education on Leadership; MBA Educational Leadership; MA/MA Professional Training & Development; Masters by research; MPhil; PhD; EdD; Post-graduate

70

Certificate in Research Methodology.

Other Courses: BA Hons Childhood Studies; BA Hons PE; MA Childhood Studies; MA PE.

PARTNERSHIPS

Leeds Metropolitan University has partnership arrangements with ca. 500 Primary and Secondary schools covering six LEAs within the Yorkshire area.

MAIN RESEARCH AND DEVELOPMENT INTERESTS

- Reading & Metacognition
- Level Descriptions & National Curriculum Assessment
- The Alexander Principle
- Citizenship & Inclusion
- OFSTED Inspection
- Assessing Work-based Learning
- Race & Curriculum
- Gender Dynamics in HE Technology Teaching
- Teacher Appraisal
- Educational Leadership
- Health Education
- Teaching & Learning in FE and HE

OTHER SPECIAL FEATURES

The University has established a School Inspection Service that is supported by full-time members of staff who have successfully undertaken OFSTED training, complemented by an extensive number of Reporting Inspectors and Team Inspectors.

LEICESTER

University of Leicester
School of Education
21 University Road
LEICESTER LE1 7RF

Tel: 0116 252 3688
Fax: 0116 252 3653
Email: soed@le.ac.uk
Website: www.le.ac.uk/education

Contact Person: Lynn Smolinski, Secretary to the School

Directions: Road: Exit 21 from M1. Take Southern Ring Road A563. At junction with A50 take left turn towards City Centre. At fourth set of traffic lights turn to University Road. School of Education is at the far end of University Road, past main University Campus, shortly after Regent Road traffic lights. British Rail: Leicester; 5 minutes by taxi.

Staff: Director: Tom Whiteside
            Teaching staff: 32 f/t; 14 p/t
            Research staff: 4

Overall FTE students in 1999/2000: 700

COURSES

ITE Primary: 1-year PGCE, age 3-8/7-11 (124); General Primary in Maths, Science, English, IT, History, Geography. Educational Psychology is a specialist option.
ITE Secondary: 1-year PGCE (187) in Maths, Biology, Chemistry, Co-ordinated Science, Physics, English, English & Communications, French, French with German, French with Italian, Geography, History, Social Science.
CPD / Higher Degrees: Modular courses offered in Leicester and various centres in Northamptonshire and other LEAs, both f/t and p/t, with a variety of outcomes - award of Certificate, Diploma, MA Professional Studies in Education, MBA in Educational Management. The Advanced Certificate in TESOL, the MA Applied Linguistics and TESOL, the MA Primary Education and the MBA in Educational Management are available by distance learning.
Other Courses: EdD with options in Educational Management, Primary Education, TESOL. The MA Applied Linguistics and TESOL can also be undertaken on a f/t or p/t basis.

PARTNERSHIPS

Both the Primary and Secondary ITE courses are steered by partnership Committees made up of representatives from the University, partnership schools and LEAs. The CPU programme arises from partnerships with neighbouring LEAs.

MAIN RESEARCH AND DEVELOPMENT INTERESTS

- Studies of Teaching & Learning Using Classroom Observation
- Evaluation Studies and the Use of New Technology
- Primary Science Education
- School Management and School Improvement
- Citizenship and Other Cross-curricular Issues
- 16-19 Education
- Language Development

University of Liverpool
Department of Education
19 Abercromby Square
LIVERPOOL L69 7ZG

Tel: 0151 794 2477
Fax: 0151 794 2512
Email: education@liv.ac.uk
Website: www.liv.ac.uk/education

Contact Person: Professor Keith Sharpe

Directions: Situated just minutes from Liverpool City Centre the University is well-served by road, rail, bus, air and ferry routes. At the end of the M62 continue straight ahead into Edge Lane (A5080 then A5047) and follow signs for Liverpool City Centre and 'The University of Liverpool'. The campus is adjacent to the Catholic Cathedral.

Staff: <u>Head of Department:</u> Professor Keith Sharpe
<u>Professors:</u>   3
<u>Other teaching staff:</u> 16 f/t; 12 p/t
<u>Research staff:</u>   8

Overall FTE students in 1999/2000:

COURSES

ITE Primary: 1-year PGCE, age 5-11 (18).
ITE KS 2/3: 1-year PGCE (30)
ITE Secondary: 1-year PGCE (124) in Maths with IT, English with Drama, MFL, Science specialising in Physics, Chemistry, Biology.
CPD / Higher Degrees: CASE; DASE; MEd; PhD; MPhil.

PARTNERSHIPS

ITT partnerships with 31 secondary schools and 30 primary schools are overseen by joint committees. Formal partnerships exist with local LEAs for CPD work and with Kidum College, Tel Aviv for the teaching and supervision of higher degrees.

MAIN RESEARCH AND DEVELOPMENT INTERESTS

- History of Education
- The Teaching of Reading

- The Internationalisation of the Curriculum
- Children's Ideas about Environmental Issues
- Computers in Science Teaching
- Changing Relationship of LEAs and Central Government
- Education Provision in Economically Stressed Inner City Areas
- Teachers' Professional Development Assessment and Evaluation
- Profiling
- The Education of the Imagination in the Visual Arts and Design
- Arts in the School Curriculum
- The Development of the Old and New Communities of Birkdale and Ainsdale
- Pupils' Conceptual Understanding of Physical and Biological Phenomena
- Teachers' Conceptions of Reading and Learning
- Assessment
- Curriculum Design
- Continuing Professional Development
- Ring Theory in Algebra / New Elementary Mathematics
- History of Mathematics
- Computers in Mathematics Teaching
- Partnership and Supervision in Primary Teacher Training
- The Development of Processes in Mathematics Thinking
- The Development of Spatial and Problem Solving Skills in Young Children
- Interprofessional Learning in Health Care Education
- Provision of Science and Engineering Education
- Teacher Supply
- Vocational Qualifications
- Children's Thinking
- Science & Technology
- MFL Teaching
- Education Policy
- The Nature of Educational Research
- Moral Development & Behaviour
- National Curriculum
- Teaching and Learning Methods in HE
- Competence-based Education & Training
- Education - Comparative, Language, History of, Geographic, Political, Science, 16-19, Further, Primary, Competence-based, Initial Teacher

OTHER SPECIAL FEATURES

Centre for Education Employment Research (CEER)
Centre for Research in Primary Science and Technology (CRIPSAT)

LIVERPOOL JM

Liverpool John Moores University
School of Education & Community Studies
I M Marsh Campus
Barkhill Road
LIVERPOOL   L17 6BD

Tel: 0151 231 5240
Fax: 0151 231 5357
Email:
Website: www.livjm.ac.uk

Contact Person: Elaine Prisk, Director of School (acting)

Directions: Within 20 minutes of M62, M56, Liverpool Lime Street Station and Liverpool Airport; 40 minutes from Manchester Airport.

Staff: <u>Director of School:</u>   Elaine Prisk (acting)
          <u>Professors:</u>   2
          <u>Other teaching staff:</u>   55 f/t; 11 p/t
          <u>Research staff/students:</u> 4/24

Overall FTE students in 1999/2000: 1725

COURSES

ITE Primary: 4-year BA QTS Hons in Primary Education (65).

ITE KS 2/3: 3-year BA/BSc QTS Hons Science Education (25), Maths Education (10), D&T (25), PE (20).

ITE Secondary: 1-year PGCE in Science (21), PE (26), MFL (25), D&T (25), Art (22); 3-year BA/BSc QTS Hons D&T (15); 4-year BA QTS Hons PE, Sport & Dance (43); 2-year BEd Hons D&T (15), Science (10), IT (20).

ITE Post-Compulsory: P/t taught Certificate in Post-16 Education (50).

CPD / Higher Degrees: Research degrees leading to MPhil/PhD; MA in Education Management, Mentoring, Science Education, SEN (80); the Inservice Unit runs many short courses, mainly self-financing, catering for local and regional needs of teachers, lecturers and others involved in education and training.

MAIN RESEARCH AND DEVELOPMENT INTERESTS

- Art Education
- Careers Guidance
- Consumer Education
- Counselling
- Dance
- Design
- Disaffection
- Earth Education
- Educational Management
- Environmental Education
- Ethnic Minorities
- Health-related Fitness & Education
- ICT in Subject Teaching
- K2/3 Progression
- Mathematics Teaching in Primary Schools
- Multi-Cultural Education
- Nutrition
- Outdoor Education
- Physical Education
- Post-16 Education
- Primary English
- Product Design
- Science Education
- Special Needs
- Teacher Professional Development
- Work-based Learning

OTHER SPECIAL FEATURES

The School incorporates staff from a wide range of disciplines and integrates teacher education, continuing education and subject-specific degrees. All degrees are part of the University's modular credit accumulation and transfer system.

LONDON GOLDSMITHS

University of London
Goldsmiths College
Department of Educational Studies
Lewisham Way, New Cross
LONDON   SE14 6NW

Tel: 0171 919 7171
Fax: 0171 919 7313
Email: educ-studies@gold.ac.uk
Website: www.gold.ac.uk

Contact Person: Department Administrator

Directions: Short walk from New Cross and New Cross Gate Stations (British Rail and Underground). Frequent rail services from Charing Cross, Waterloo and London Bridge (ca. 15 minutes).

Staff: <u>Head of Department:</u> Professor Clyde Chitty
             <u>Teaching staff:</u>   27 f/t; 11 p/t
             <u>Research staff:</u>   3

Overall FTE students in 1999/2000: 800

COURSES

ITE Primary: 1-year PGCE, age 3-11 (60); 3-year BA(Ed) Hons, age 3-11 (89) in Art, D&T with Computing, English, Humanities, Maths with Computing, Nursery, PE, Science.
ITE Secondary: 4-year BA(Ed) D&T (16); 1-year PGCE (265) in Art, D&T, Drama, English, Geography, Maths, MFL (French, German, Spanish), Music, Science, Social Sciences.
CPD / Higher Degrees: Varied programme of inservice courses and consultancies with provision of MA accreditation; courses for returners, familiarisation for overseas-trained teachers and Graduate and Registered Teachers programme; 1-year f/t or 2-5 years p/t (or approved combination of both) modular MA Education in a range of educational fields; supervision available for f/t or p/t MPhil, PhD.

PARTNERSHIPS

The Goldsmiths Primary Partnership (BAEd, PGCE) works in full partnership with ca. 100 LEA- and grant-maintained schools in the Greater London area.

Supervision of students is shared equally between school- and college-based tutors. The PGCE Secondary Programme works in partnership with ca. 90 schools across Greater London (mainly in the South-East) where each student receives a whole-school programme in school and weekly tutorial programme via their school-based tutor in each subject area. Both Primary and Secondary Partnerships provide on-going training and support groups for all tutors. CPD works in close partnership with schools, LEAs and other educational organisations. Partnership is central to the identification and assessment of professional needs, design, planning and delivery, monitoring and evaluation and accreditation of CPD.

MAIN RESEARCH AND DEVELOPMENT INTERESTS

- Art & Design in Education
- Bilingualism & Biculturalism
- Classroom Enquiry
- Curriculum Studies
- Design & Technology
- Early Childhood Education
- Early Literacy
- Educational Management
- English & Media in Education
- Equal Opportunities Education
- ICT
- Language & Literature
- Personal & Social Development of Children and Young People (Citizenship/PSHE)
- Policy Studies
- Research Methodology
- Sociology of Education
- Special Educational Needs
- Teacher Education
- Partnership & Mentoring
- Inclusive Education
- Comprehensive Education

OTHER SPECIAL FEATURES

Centre for Cross-Curricular Initiatives; Goldsmiths Journal of Education

LONDON INSTITUTE

Institute of Education
University of London
20 Bedford Way
LONDON WC1H 0AL

Tel: 0171 580 1122
Fax: 0171 612 6097
Email: l.loughran@ioe.ac.uk
Website: www.ioe.ac.uk

Contact Person: Dr Loreto Loughran, Academic Registrar and Head of International Development

Directions: Nearest Underground station: Russell Square (Piccadilly Line), 5 minutes walk from the Institute.

Staff: Director of Institute: Professor Peter Mortimore, OBE
             Professors: 25
             Other teaching staff: 99 f/t; 58 p/t
             Research staff/students: 129/662

Overall FTE students in 1999/2000: 2260

COURSES

ITE Primary: 1-year PGCE, age 3-8 in English, Maths, Science, 7-11 in History, Geography, Art & Design, D&T, Maths, Music (192); 5-term p/t PGCE, age 3-8 or 7-11 (50).

ITE Secondary: 1-year PGCE in Art & Design, Business & Economics, English, English with Drama, Geography, History, IT, Maths, MFL (French, Spanish, German), Music, RE, Science Education, Social Sciences with Humanities (745).

ITE Post-Compulsory: 1-year PGCE for those wishing to teach in Sixth Form Colleges and FE Colleges (120); 2-year p/t FE Teacher's Certificate course   (c. 25).

CPD / Higher Degrees: Wide range of specialist diplomas; Advanced Diploma in Education; Advanced Diploma in Professional Studies; 45 MA courses; Inservice BEd; Associateship programmes; Special Course programmes; MPhil; PhD; EdD.

Other Courses: Professional training in Educational Psychology; wide range of short courses (some counting towards awards); many outreach courses for those teaching in primary, secondary, further or adult education; professional and certificate courses in English for Academic Purposes.

PARTNERSHIPS

Partnership with schools and further education colleges for ITT.

MAIN RESEARCH AND DEVELOPMENT INTERESTS

- Policy
- Administration & Management from School to National Level
- Teacher Training & Practice
- Curriculum Content & Teaching (individual subjects and cross-curricular topics)
- Assessment, Testing & Evaluation
- Learning Skills & Process
- School Effectiveness & Improvement
- Child Development, Family Functioning & Health Education
- Special Needs
- International Comparisons & Studies
- Research Methods & Techniques
- Languages in Education
- Use of ICT
- Post-Compulsory Education

OTHER SPECIAL FEATURES

The Institute has a number of major research centres and units and a Leadership Centre for the professional development of school leaders. A Centre for Future Learning is being established which will provide the focus for collaborative experimentation in, and evaluation of, new ways of teaching and learning which exploit developments in information and communication technology. The Institute is the only School of Education in the UK to achieve the top ranking in each of the national research assessment exercises.

LONDON KING'S

University of London
King's College
School of Education
Franklin Wilkins Building
Waterloo Road
LONDON   SE1 8WA

Tel: 020 7848 3167
Fax: 020 7848 3182
Email: nicola.meza@kcl.ac.uk
Website: www.kcl.ac.uk/education

Contact Person: Departmental Administrator

Directions: Nearest station: Waterloo (British Rail and Underground - Bakerloo and Northern lines)

Staff: Head of School: Professor Dylan Wiliam
             Professors: 10
             Teaching staff: 25 f/t; 3 p/t
             Research Staff: 12

Overall FTE students in 1999/2000: 434

COURSES

ITE Secondary: 4-year concurrent BSc/PGCE in Education with Maths and Physics; 4-year concurrent BA/PGCE in Education and MFL; PGCE (220) in Biology, Chemistry, Classics, English, French, German, IT, Maths, Physics, RE, Spanish.

CPD / Higher Degrees: F/t or p/t Masters courses in RE, Theology & Education, Health Promotion & Education, Applied Language Studies in Education, Classics Education, Computers in Education, Maths Education, Science Education, Education Management, Urban Education, English in Education, MFL, Youth Ministry & Education; f/t or p/t postgraduate diploma courses in Health Education, Health Promotion; f/t or p/t MPhil; f/t or p/t PhD; p/t EdD; f/t or p/t MRes in Social Sciences.

PARTNERSHIPS

The School has developed good relations with schools and LEAs throughout the country which has enabled it to build up its extensive research profile.

MAIN RESEARCH AND DEVELOPMENT INTERESTS

• Learning Processes: Funded research in this area includes the programme of cognitive acceleration in science and mathematics and the Leverhulme Numeracy Research Programme which comprises six inter-linked projects investigating effective teaching of numeracy in primary schools. Much of the work is conducted in close partnership with teachers and schools.

• Professional Change & Professional Development: The broad aim of research, concentrated almost exclusively on education and health professionals, is to understand professional roles and practices.

• Policy & Change: Funded studies include those on parental choice, secondary education markets and school values, the dynamics of post-16 education and training markets and choice of Higher Education.

• Assessment: Includes foundational philosophical issues through practical applications to the development and implementation of assessment materials.

• Religion & Culture: Work is taking place on charismatic movements, spirituality, religion and post-modernism and the theological education of professional ministers of religion, teachers and advisers.

• Education & New Media: The emphasis in this research area is on synergistic links between studies in diverse areas, eg the influence of film on students' appreciation of literature, the use of ICT in higher education, theories of learning and the design of educational software, language and ICT, the implications of 'new literacies' for languages in education.

OTHER SPECIAL FEATURES

The School of Education has an international reputation for the quality of its research, curriculum development and teaching. The School has achieved the highest possible research rating in all three national Research Assessment Exercises, one of only two departments of Education in the UK to achieve this distinction.

Loughborough University
Department of Education
Ashby Road
LOUGHBOROUGH   LE11 3TU

Tel: 01509 222763
Fax: 01509 223912
Email: s.d.bryman@lboro.ac.uk
Website: www.lboro.ac.uk/departments/ed

Contact Person: Sue Bryman

Directions: Road: Exit from M1 signposted Loughborough to eastbound. At second roundabout turn right for main entrance to University campus. On campus follow signs to Education which is housed in the Matthew Arnold Building. British Rail: Loughborough; 10 minutes by taxi.

Staff: Head of Department: Dr Phil Wild
          Professors: 3
          Other teaching staff: 12 f/t; 8 p/t
          Research staff: 4

Overall FTE students in 1999/2000:

COURSES

ITE Primary: 1-year PGCE, age 5-11 (38) with emphasis on KS2, age 7-11.

ITE Secondary: 1-year PGCE (149) in IT, Science with Biology, Chemistry or Physics, D&T, English, Maths, PE; 3-year BSc Hons in Maths with Education (22) or Industrial D&T with Education (50) offering subsequent entry to PGCE.

CPD / Higher Degrees: Modular MA in Education; Diplomas and Certificates of Further Professional Study; MSc in Mathematical Education, combining teaching with other University departments; MPhil/PhD by research; MA programme through MA summer programme and/or credit transfer with other institutions of HE; accredited MA courses based in schools and in partnership with LEAs.

Other Courses: Short courses and teacher fellowships may be negotiated with schools and LEAs; Summer School; Contracts Teacher day and other negotiated inservice for particular groups of clients; Certificate in Professional Studies for professionals concerned with EBD Schools.

PARTNERSHIPS

The Secondary ITE courses are delivered in partnership with 60 local schools within a 25 mile radius of the University. The primary ITE course involves over 20 local schools. Partner schools provide all trainees with teaching experience in two different kinds of school during their placements. Trained mentors provide professional subject support during a school experience of both serial and block practices which are closely related to the University-based elements of the course.

A modular postgraduate programme offering a range of specialist options is provided in Peterborough, in partnership with Peterbrough City Council and the Greater Peterborough Chamber of Commerce Training and Enterprise. Certificate, Diploma and MA awards can be obtained through this programme.

MAIN RESEARCH AND DEVELOPMENT INTERESTS

- Information & Communication Technology
- School Improvement & Classroom-based Research & Development
- Mathematical Education
- Special Needs
- Social Policy, Management & Education
- Science Education
- The Psychology of Education

MANCHESTER

University of Manchester
School of Education
Humanities Building
Oxford Road
MANCHESTER M13 9PL

Tel: 0161 275 3553
Fax: 0161 275 3552
Email: t.christie@man.ac.uk
Website: www.man.ac.uk

Contact Person: Jo Peers, Faculty Secretary

Directions: Road: M6, M62, M61 close by. British Rail: 15 minutes from Piccadilly Station. Air: 20 minutes by taxi to Manchester Airport.

Staff: Director of School: Professor Tom Christie
Professors: 11.8 FTE
Other teaching staff: 64 FTE
Research staff & students: 18 RA, 160 PhD

Overall FTE students in 1999/2000: 1165

COURSES

ITE Primary: 1-year PGCE (63).
ITE Secondary: 1-year PGCE in English, Maths, Science, D&T, IT, MFL, Business Studies (210).
CPD / Higher Degrees: Certificate incl. Counselling; TESOL; MEd; MPhil; MSc Research Methods (ESRC-approved); MPhil; EdD; PhD.
Other Courses: NPQH; LPSH; Headlamp; Teaching Studies; BA Human Education; BA Leisure Management; BA Education; BSc Speech & Language Thearpy.

PARTNERSHIPS

Active ITT partnership with some 150 schools in the Greater Manchester area and beyond. Joint school improvement initiatives with five LEAs. The Teaching Studies Programme provides a minimum two-year support. Continuing Professional Development of teachers in schools and colleges is supported through short courses culminating to APEL in the MEd. The Centre for Educational Leadership provides headship training and development throughout the north-west region for aspiring and newly appointed headteachers and is one of seven national providers of the Leadership Programme for Serving Headteachers.

The Faculty is currently engaged in a number of collaborative research and evaluation studies with LEAs in the region and nationally.

MAIN RESEARCH AND DEVELOPMENT INTERESTS

- Teaching & Learning, especially Maths Education, ICT in ELT
- Lifelong & Workbased Learning, especially Leisure Industries
- Leadership & Management, especially Curriculum and Assessment
- Speech, Language & Communication (includes Speech Therapy, Deafness)
- Special & Inclusive Education (includes Hester Adrian Research Centre)
- Education, Health & Social Development (includes Ethnic Studies)

OTHER SPECIAL FEATURES

Over 90% research-active staff, 28 holding research funds totalling £1.6 million for 1999/2000.

MANCHESTER MET

Manchester Metropolitan University
Institute of Education

I. Crewe Campus
Crewe Green Road
CREWE CW1 5DU

II. Didsbury Campus
799 Wilmslow Road
MANCHESTER M20 2RR

Tel: 0161 247 5192	**Tel:**	0161 247 2008
Fax: 0161 247 6370	**Fax:**	0161 247 6368
Email: d.burton@mmu.ac.uk	**Email:**	c.walker@mmu.ac.uk

Website: www.mmu.ac.uk

Contact Person: Mrs Christine Walker

Directions: *Crewe:* Road: Easy access from M6 (J17 from N, J16 from S). Rail: Crewe; 5 minutes walk. *Didsbury:* Road: Easy access from M56 (J1) and M60 (J3). Rail: Half-hourly service from Manchester Piccadilly to East Didsbury; 5 minutes walk.

Staff:

Institute Director:	Professor K Leni Oglesby (acting)
Professors:	7
Other teaching staff:	150 f/t; 210 p/t
Research staff/students:	21/35

Overall FTE students in 1999/2000: 4170

COURSES

ITE Primary: *Crewe:* 4-year BA Hons (153) in English, Maths, Science (Environmental/Life), Geography, History, IT, PE; 1-year PGCE (76) for early and junior years. *Didsbury:* 4-year BEd Hons (262) Art & Design, Drama, English, Geography, History, Maths, Music, Religious Studies, Science, Technology, Numeracy & Literacy with SEN, Advanced Early Years Studies; 1-year PGCE (120) Early Years, Lower Primary, Upper Primary.

ITE KS 2/3: *Didsbury:* 2-year PGCE (55) in English, Maths, Science, MFL, D&T.

ITE Secondary: *Crewe:* 3-year BA/BSc Hons (50) in Business Education, D&T, Geography, Maths, PE, Science (Life/Environmental); 2-year BEd Hons (50) in Business Education, D&T; 2-year PGCE (20) D&T; 1-year PGCE (120) Business Education, D&T, English, Geography, General Science, MFL, RE, PE. *Didsbury:* 3-year BEd/BEd Hons Maths (10); 1-year PGCE (471) in Art & Design, Drama, English, English with SEN; Geography, History, Maths,

French, German, Spanish, Music, RE, Biology, Chemistry, Physics, Social Studies, D&T/Food Technology; 2-year PGCE Maths (15); 2-year BEd Hons Maths (5); 2-year PGCE Music (15) (with Royal Northern College of Music). **CPD / Higher Degrees:** A wide range of award-bearing courses, from Certificate to Masters and EdD, for teachers and other professionals. Research degrees (MPhil, PhD). Range of short courses, conferences, workshops, commissioned CPD, school/LEA-based services.

Other Courses: Cert Ed/PGCE (FAHE); BA Hons Early Childhood Studies.

PARTNERSHIPS

Partnership with 800 primary schools and 410 secondary schools and colleges for ITT. Strong school, LEA and college partnership links for CPD. Strong partnerships with FE colleges for the development of teaching and learning in FAHE. Member of the North West NPQH Assessment Partnership. Environmental Management in Education consortium with the Groundwork Trust and colleges.

MAIN RESEARCH AND DEVELOPMENT INTERESTS

- Development Education
- Early Years/Educare
- Educational Management and School Improvement
- Environmental Education
- Equal Opportunities & Ethnic Minorities in Education
- Home-school links
- Learning Styles
- Literacy & Numeracy
- Mathematics Education and Sciences Education
- Post-Compulsory and Vocational Education & Training
- Practitioner Research
- Professional Development/Training Schools
- Research Methodology
- Special Educational Needs

MIDDLESEX

Middlesex University
School of Lifelong Learning & Education
Trent Park
Bramley Road
LONDON N14 4YZ

Tel: 0181 362 6367
Fax: 0181 362 6147
Email: r.tufnell@mdx.ac.uk
Website: www.mdx.ac.uk
Contact Person: Professor Richard Tufnell, Dean

Directions: Road: Exit 24 from M25 to London/Southgate for 3 miles, south entry of Trent Park Country Park, through park to University Campus. After parking, follow signs to Mansion Buildings. British Rail: Oakwood. Middlesex University minibus service to campus can be picked up at the top of the drive (Snakes Lane) every 10 minutes in term time.

Staff: Head of School: Professor Richard Tufnell

No current information submitted for this edition. Please contact Middlesex University directly or refer to their website.

NEWCASTLE

University of Newcastle
Department of Education
St Thomas' Street
NEWCASTLE UPON TYNE   NE1 7RU

Tel: 0191 222 6000
Fax: 0191 222 6553
Email: w.f.dennison@ncl.ac.uk
Website: www.ncl.ac.uk/neduc

Contact Person: Dr W F Dennison

Directions: Road: Exit City (North) from A6127 (M) and follow signs to University. St Thomas' Street is at the southern end of the campus. British Rail: Newcastle upon Tyne; 5 minutes by taxi.

Staff: Head of Department: Dr W F Dennison
              Professors: 5
              Other teaching staff: 34 f/t; 8 p/t
              Research staff: 8

Overall FTE students in 1999/2000: 550

COURSES

ITE Primary: 1-year PGCE, age 3-11 (67)
ITE KS 2/3: 1-year PGCE, age 7-14 (55) in Maths, Science, MFL.
ITE Secondary: 1-year PGCE (198) in Maths, Sciences, French, German, RE, English, Geography, History, Spanish.
CPD / Higher Degrees: Certificate, MEd, EdD (taught doctorate); MPhil; PhD; extensive range of short courses for schools.
Other Courses: Centre for International Studies in Education; Testamur in English Studies for Norwegian Teachers; MSc in Educational Psychology.

PARTNERSHIPS

All teaching experience in Partnership schools (140). Partnership liaison committees for Primary and Secondary sectors (CPD and ITE). The Department is also closely linked with a number of EAZs (Education Action Zones) located in the North-East of England.

MAIN RESEARCH AND DEVELOPMENT INTERESTS

The research interests of the Department are concentrated on key areas:

- School Effectiveness & Improvement
- Special Needs and Social/Education Inclusion
- Thinking Skills
- Early Childhood
- Higher Education Research
- Learning & Instruction
- Educational Policy
- ICT & Pedagogy

OTHER SPECIAL FEATURES

The Department houses both the Northern Region NPQH Training and Development Centre and the NPQH Asssessment Centre. The Department is also a member of the CCDU/Capita/Newcastle University consortia for the provision of LPSH programmes.

The Department, in partnership with the MARI organisation and several LEAs, is closely involved with the NOF ICT initiative for teachers.

NEWMAN

Newman College of Higher Education
Genners Lane
BIRMINGHAM   B32 3NT

Tel: 0121 476 1181
Fax: 0121 476 1196
Email: c.wilkinson@newman.ac.uk
Website: www.newman.ac.uk

Contact Person: Christine Wilkinson, Admissions Registrar

Directions: Road: Located on south-west side of Birmingham, close to Junction 3 of the M5. Rail: Birmingham New Street; No 22 bus.

Staff: Principal: Ms Kate Kershaw

No current information submitted for this edition. Please contact Newman College directly or refer to their website.

NEWMAN

NEWPORT

University of Wales College, Newport
Department of Teacher Education
Caerleon Campus, PO Box 179
NEWPORT NP18 3YG

Tel: 01633 432242
Fax: 01633 432074
Email: fiona.illing@newport.ac.uk
Website: www.newport.ac.uk

Contact Person: Ms Fiona Illing, Departmental Administrator

Directions: Road: Via the M4 to Newport (Junction 25 from east, Junction 26 from west). The Caerleon Campus is sign-posted from the M4. Rail: Newport. Take no 2 bus from stand 24 of Newport central bus station to Caerleon.

Staff: Head of Department: Dr Muriel Adams
Teaching staff: 23 f/t; 10 p/t

Overall FTE students in 1999/2000: 545

COURSES

ITE Primary: 1-year PGCE, age 5-11 (40); 3-year BA Hons, age 5-11 (103).
ITE Secondary: 1-year PGCE D&T; 2-year BSc D&T; 2-year BSc Maths with Science; 2-year BSc Maths with ICT; 3-year BA Hons D&T (total secondary 59)
CPD / Higher Degrees: Certificate; Diploma; BA (Education); MA (Education); extensive range of short courses for primary schools; expertise in SEN and Educational Management.

PARTNERSHIPS

122 schools in primary partnership, 120 English-medium, two Welsh-medium. Located mainly in the Welsh county boroughs of Blaenau Gwent, Caerphilly, Torfaen, Monmouthshire and Newport. A termly Schools/UWCN Forum takes place in each of the above county boroughs at which matters to do with ITT and CPD are discussed. 61 schools in secondary partnership of which five teach through the medium of Welsh covering a wide geographic area across South Wales and the English border counties.

MAIN RESEARCH AND DEVELOPMENT INTERESTS

- Assessment, Recording and Reporting at KS 1/2
- Using ICT in Initial Teacher Training
- Primary School Management
- Special Educational Needs
- The Welsh Dimension in the Curriculum
- Continuing Professional Development

OTHER SPECIAL FEATURES

Schools' Inspection Unit for Primary and Special Schools.

NEWI

North East Wales Institute of Higher Education
School of Education & Humanities
Crispin Lane Buildings
Crispin Lane
WREXHAM   LL11 2AW

Tel: 01978 293234
Fax: 01978 293311
Email: a.edwards@newi.ac.uk
Website: www.newi.ac.uk

Contact Person: Secretary to Head of School

Directions: NEWI campus, Mold/Wrexham signposted road off Wrexham bypass. First turning left off second roundabout to NEWI campus.

Staff: Head of School: Mr Philip Bassett
              Teaching staff: 18 f/t
              Research staff: 3

Overall FTE students in 1999/2000: 420

COURSES

ITE Primary: 3-year BA Hons QTS Primary, age 3-8/7-12 (84)
ITE Post-Compulsory: PGCE (25)
CPD / Higher Degrees: Certificate, MA(Ed) (taught plus dissertation); MPhil; PhD; training and education agency (NEWETA); Post-graduate Certificate in Professional Development in HE (ILT-linked).
Other Courses: Welsh as a first and second language at a range of levels, on site and in the community.

PARTNERSHIPS

A partnership model of training has been developed with 140 primary schools in Wrexham, Flintshire, Denbighshire, Conwy, Shropshire, Merseyside and Cheshire.

MAIN RESEARCH AND DEVELOPMENT INTERESTS

- Citizenship
- School Improvement
- Thinking Skills in the Primary School
- Numeracy & Literacy
- The Development of Early Years Education
- Early Years
- Special Needs
- Physical Education within the Primary Course
- Teaching Qualification for Higher Education
- Non-QTS Education Courses
- Education in Business and the Community

NORTH LONDON

University of North London
School of Education
166-220 Holloway Road
LONDON   N7 8DB

Tel: 0171 753 5104
Fax: 0171 753 5400
Email: j.kazemzadeh@unl.ac.uk
Website: www.unl.ac.uk

Contact Person: Julien Kazemzadeh, Senior School Administrator

Directions: Nearest underground station: Holloway Road (Piccadilly Line). Exit station and turn right on Holloway Road. The School of Education is situated in the Tower Building on the opposite side of the road. Nearest railway stations: King's Cross, Finsbury Park, Drayton Park.

Staff: Head of School: Mr Ian Menter
           Professors: 1
           Other teaching staff: 36 f/t; 3 p/t
           Research staff & students: 15

Overall FTE students in 1999/2000: 770

COURSES

ITE Primary: 1-year PGCE (multilingual), age 3-8 (41); 4-year BEd Hons, age 3-8/7-11 (104 first year intake).
ITE Secondary: PGCE MFL (French, German, Italian, Spanish) (27), English with Media (45); 2-year shortened BA Maths (first year intake 9); 1- and 2-year PGCE Maths (9); 2-year shortened BA/PGCE Music (first year intake 10).
CPD / Higher Degrees: TTA-funded inservice courses leading to a range of diplomas in Professional Development in Education.
Other Courses: BA Humanities (60/year) for Education Studies, half degree; p/t Early Childhood Studies Scheme modular evening course leading to Certificate, Diploma or BA with or without Honours; MA Education including MA Education (Managing School Improvement) and MA Early Education with Care (Pen Green Centre); PhD; extensive range of short courses for schools and LEAs.

PARTNERSHIPS

Working with more than 200 nursery/primary schools and approximately 40 secondary schools on a multi-level partnership scheme. Employment-based routes into teaching with the Agency for Jewish Education. Access links with numerous colleges in London.

MAIN RESEARCH AND DEVELOPMENT INTERESTS

- Parental Involvement in Education (especially Maths education and children's writing)
- Children's Economic, Social & Industrial Understanding (including European Thematic Network)
- Urban Education
- Early Learning
- Multilingualism
- Teacher Education & Teacher Supply in London

OTHER SPECIAL FEATURES

- Edits Primary Teaching Studies.
- School-based INSET & consultancy through the Core Consultancy Unit.
- Information Technology training & support services through the IT Learning Exchange.
- Links with SUNY, USA.
- Involvement in European projects on Intercultural Education.

NORTHAMPTON

University College Northampton
Faculty of Arts & Social Science
School of Education
Park Campus, Boughton Green Road
NORTHAMPTON NN2 7AL

Tel: 01604 735500
Fax: 01604 713759
Email: jon.davison@northampton.ac.uk
Website: www.nene.ac.uk

Contact Person: Susan Robertson, School Secretary

Directions: Map available on request.

Staff: Head of School: Professor Jon Davison
Professors: 1
Other teaching staff: 32 f/t; 3 p/t
Research staff & students: 6

Overall FTE students in 1999/2000: 950

COURSES

ITE Primary: 1-year PGCE, age 5-11 (60); 3-year BA QTS, age 5-11 (408) in Maths, English, Science, Art, History, PE; 3-year BA QTS Early Years Education, age 3-8 (16). All courses run in partnership with local schools.
CPD / Higher Degrees: MA Professional Studies; Diploma in Professional Studies in Education; RSA Diploma and Certificate Courses; Certificate in Education course; various other short courses.
Other Courses: Combined Honours, Education Studies (non-QTS); BA Hons Early Childhood Studies (non-QTS).

PARTNERSHIPS

In partnership with over 300 primary schools in Northamptonshire, Buckinghamshire, Cambridgeshire, Leicestershire, Warwickshire.

MAIN RESEARCH AND DEVELOPMENT INTERESTS

- Special Educational Needs
- Policy for Inclusion
- Lifelong Learning
- Literacy & Young Children
- Information Technology in Education
- Supporting the Subject-Coordinator in Primary Schools
- Monitoring National Curriculum Art
- Staff Development

University of Northumbria at Newcastle
Faculty of Health, Social Work & Education
Coach Lane Campus
NEWCASTLE UPON TYNE   NE7 7XA

Tel: 0191 227 4514
Fax: 0191 227 4419
Email: patrick.easen@unn.ac.uk
Website: www.unn.ac.uk

Contact Person: Professor Patrick Easen

Directions: Road: Exit city motorway east (for Tynemouth) to Coast Road (A1058); slip road to Walker after ca. 2 miles; left at lights into Red Hall Drive, then Coach Lane; campus 600 yards north on left. Rail: Newcastle Central; 10 minutes by taxi.

Staff: Head of School: Professor Patrick Easen
            Teaching staff: 45 f/t
            Research staff: 3

Overall FTE students in 1999/2000: 709

COURSES

ITE Primary: 1-year PGCE, age 3-8/7-11 (70); 3-year BA Hons QTS, age 3-8/7-11 (270).

ITE Secondary: 1-year PGCE (80) in Art, Maths, MFL, PE, Science, Technology (CTD), Technology (Home Economics); 2-year BA Hons/PGCE routes in Art, Maths, MFL, Science, Technology (90).

CPD / Higher Degrees: Advanced Diploma/BA; Postgraduate Certificate/Diploma/MEd including specialist routes in early years, SEN, primary curriculum subjects; Certificate/Diploma/MEd in University Teaching and Learning; MPhil; PhD; range of short courses and consultancy, both campus and school-based, particularly in primary curriculum subjects, early years education and special educational needs.

Other Courses: Lindisfarne Initial Teacher Training (Managing Agent); MA for Israeli teachers; Doctoral programme in tertiary education in Thailand; short and award-bearing courses in Malaysia.

PARTNERSHIPS

Initial teacher training partnerships with large number and wide range of schools in the North East region, including nursery, first, primary, middle and secondary schools. CPD partnerships with most LEAs in the North east region, including award-bearing courses, Standards Fund courses, specialist Centres, Education Action Zones, project development and research and evaluation activity. CPD partnerships with FE colleges, industry, business and other training organisations in relation to FE and training courses.

MAIN RESEARCH AND DEVELOPMENT INTERESTS

- Early Years Education
- Special Educational Needs
- Training Partnerships
- Career-entry Profiles & the Induction of New Teachers
- Professional Development & Organisational Education
- Teaching, Learning & Assessment in Higher Education
- Multiprofessional Training & Provision

OTHER SPECIAL FEATURES

- Located in Faculty, providing range of training for different professions, including nursing, midwifery, physiotherapy and occupational therapy and social work.
- Specialist Centres for Vocational Education & Training and for Advances in Higher Education.
- Range of international links including Europe, Middle East and South East Asia.

NOTTINGHAM

University of Nottingham
School of Education
Jubilee Campus
NOTTINGHAM   NG8 1BB

Tel: 0115 951 5151
Fax: 0115 979 1506
Email: david.hopkins@nottingham.ac.uk
Website: www.nott.ac.uk

Contact Person: Rachel Crowley

Directions: Road: Exit 25 from M1; campus is 4 miles east of A52; School is located in the Educational Building in centre of campus, adjacent to Main Library. Rail: Nottingham station; 10 minutes by taxi. Air: East Midland; 9 miles via M1 and A52.

Staff: Dean of Faculty: Professor David Hopkins
             Teaching staff: 34 f/t; 12 p/t
             Research staff: 10

Overall FTE students in 1999/2000: 580

COURSES

ITE Secondary: 1-year PGCE (340) in English, Science (Biology, Chemistry, Physics), Geography, History, Mathematics, MFL (French, German, Japanese, Russian, Spanish, European PGCE).
CPD / Higher Degrees: MPhil/PhD by research; EdD (Teacher Education or School Improvement); Dip/MA/MEd (1 year f/t, 2 years p/t or by credit accumulation) specialising in Human Relations, Teaching, Special Needs, English Language Teaching, Counselling Studies, Professional Development & School Improvement, Children's Literature, Management in Education, International Education Professionals, other options; Inservice short courses for teachers, accreditation, consultancy and inspection services.

PARTNERSHIPS

Partnerships exist with over 90 schools in Nottinghamshire, Derbyshire and Lincolnshire. The link between ITE, CPD and school improvement is being explored through redefined partnerships between the schools and the University.

MAIN RESEARCH AND DEVELOPMENT INTERESTS

- Action Research
- Assessment & Evaluation
- Continuing Professional Development
- Counselling
- Educational Management
- Educational Psychology
- Higher Education Development in Teaching & Learning
- Human Relations
- Key Skills
- Language & Literacy
- Mathematics Education
- School Improvement
- Social & Urban Policy
- Teacher Thinking
- TESOL

OTHER SPECIAL FEATURES

The School has re-organised its Advanced Course programme around a flexible modular structure. There are now opportunities for teachers to complete a range of awards through an integrated programme of modules. There is also a scheme for accrediting prior learning and for accrediting LEA courses through a scheme developed initially in partnership with LEAs. The School runs an International Summer School Masters programme and a taught EdD programme in School Improvement. There is a UK based course and an overseas course (Hong Kong and South Africa).

The School offers an NQT programme and accredits mentor work. Both of these schemes lead students into innovative MA Teaching.

NOTTINGHAM TRENT

The Nottingham Trent University
Faculty of Education
Clifton Hall, Clifton Village
NOTTINGHAM   NG11 8NJ

Tel: 01158 486767
Fax: 01158 486747
Email: anna.burrows@ntu.ac.uk
Website: www.ntu.ac.uk

Contact Person: Anna Burrows

Directions: Road: *Primary Department, Faculty Office and CPD Office* (Clifton Hall): M1 Junction 24, A453 towards Nottingham; pass the City boundary and turn left into Clifton Village and follow on to Clifton Hall. *Secondary and Tertiary Department:* Clifton Campus (Inservice Centre): M1 Junction 24, A453 towards Nottingham; Campus on left, 100m after turn for Clifton Village. City Campus (Barnes Wallis Building): Nottingham City Centre, Shakespeare Street. Rail: Nottingham.

Staff: Dean of Faculty: Professor Nigel Hastings
           Professors: 4
           Other teaching staff: 55 f/t; 50 p/t
           Research staff/students: 4/26

Overall FTE students in 1999/2000: 1200

COURSES

ITE Primary: 1-year PGCE, age 5-11 (48) in all primary curriculum areas; 4-year BA Hons Specialist Primary Education, age 5-11 (120) in English, Maths, Science, Humanities, PE, D&T, IT, Early Years, age 3-8.
ITE Secondary: 1-year PGCE, age 11-18 (65) in Business Education, D&T Education, English, Maths, Science; 2-year BA Hons Business Education, BSc Hons D&T Education, age 11-18 (60); 4-year BSc Hons D&T Education, age 11-18 (35).
ITE Post-Compulsory: F/t CertEd/PGCE: FE (50); p/t CertEd/PGCE: FET (100).

CPD / Higher Degrees: The CPD programme offers a flexible, modular p/ t provision for practising teachers, lecturers and other professionals involved in education and training. Qualifications include: MA, Advanced Graduate Diploma, BA Hons Education, Certificate in Professional Studies in Education; MPhil; PhD.

Other Courses: BSc Hons Business & Technology (40); BA Hons Psychology & Educational Development (60); BA Hons Business, Leisure & Sport Education (20); BA Hons Business & Environmental Education (20).

PARTNERSHIPS

All our ITT courses are now in full and flourishing partnership arrangements with schools and colleges in the region, in which many students are subsequently offered employment. These relationships also support and benefit from the University's extensive range of CPD activities.

MAIN RESEARCH AND DEVELOPMENT INTERESTS

- Developing Primary Practice (especially class management and curriculum specialisms art, science, maths, language)
- Education for Work (partnership, business education, key skills)
- Social Justice & Differentiation (especially entitlement, access, development/environmental issues)
- CPD (teacher education, distance learning, impact on pupil learning)
- Teaching & Learning in HE (methodological issues, action research, theory/ practice, intervention research, ethics)

OPEN UNIVERSITY

Open University
School of Education
Walton Hall
MILTON KEYNES   MK7 6AA

Tel: 01908 652896
Fax: 01908 858429
Email: g.shacklock@open.ac.uk
Website: www.open.ac.uk

Contact Person: Mr Will Swann, Dean and Director of Studies

Directions:

Staff: Dean of School: Mr Will Swann
Professors: 7
Other teaching staff: 80 f/t, 10 p/t
Research staff & students: 19/51

Overall students (p/t) in 1999/2000: 9798

COURSES

CPD / Higher Degrees: Undergraduate level professional development courses; undergraduate Diploma in English Language Studies, advanced diplomas, MA in Education; EdD (taught doctorate); MPhil; PhD.
Other Courses: Specialist Teacher Assistant Certificate (STAC); National Professional Qualification for Headship (NPQH); Professional Development for Special Educational Needs Coordinators; ICT courses.

PARTNERSHIPS

The STAC courses are presented in collaboration with LEAs. The University is involved in collaborative teaching schemes in North and South America, Australia and South East Asia.

MAIN RESEARCH AND DEVELOPMENT INTERESTS

The School of Education has six centres that focus on research:
* Centre for Sociology & Social Research
* Centre for Educational Policy & Management
* Centre for Human Development & Learning
* Centre for Language & Communication

110

- Centre for Curriculum & Teaching Studies
- Centre for Research & Development in Teacher Education

OTHER SPECIAL FEATURES

The Open University provides part-time supported open learning courses for a wide range of education professionals, parents and governors. We cover the whole of the UK, BFPO and some parts of Europe.

OXFORD

University of Oxford
Department of Educational Studies
15 Norham Gardens
OXFORD   OX2 6PY

Tel: 01865 274024
Fax: 01865 274027
Email: enquiries@edstud.ox.ac.uk
Website: http://units.ox.ac.uk/depts/edstud

Contact Person: Ms Clare Atkinson, Administrator

Directions: Norham Gardens is just off Banbury Road at the St Giles end.

Staff: <u>Head of Department:</u> Professor Richard Pring
             <u>Professors:</u>   2
             <u>Other teaching staff</u>: 16 f/t; 4 p/t
             <u>Research staff</u>:   10

Overall FTE students in 1999/2000: 270

COURSES

ITE Secondary: 1-year PGCE (150) in Maths, Biology, Chemistry, Physics, English, Geography, History, MFL. All students are required to take a short course in ICT. Subsidiary subjects: SEN, Education in Developing Countries, Drama, Teaching Games Skills in Schools, Museums as an Educational Resource.

CPD / Higher Degrees: 2-year p/t Postgraduate Diploma in Educational Studies in Developing Science Education in Secondary Schools, Developing Teaching as a Research-based Profession, Improving Writing on a Whole School Basis at KS 2/3, Teaching Science Effectively in Primary Schools, Supporting the Learning of NQTs (Primary and Secondary Phase), Mentoring in ITE, Developing Maths Teaching, Enquiry-based Learning in Geography; 1-year f/t taught MSc in Educational Research Methodology ('A-rated' by ESRC) and in Comparative and International Education; 2-year p/t taught course in Educational Studies; f/t and   p/t research programmes for the MLitt and DPhil. The Department has been given Mode A recognition by ESRC for the training of ESRC funded research students.

112

PARTNERSHIPS

The Oxford Internship Scheme is a well established ITT partnership between the University, Oxfordshire LEA and maintained schools in Oxfordshire, Wiltshire and Northants. The Department also works in partnership with Oxfordshire LEA and schools in the planning and delivery of both award-bearing and non award-bearing CPD courses.

MAIN RESEARCH AND DEVELOPMENT INTERESTS

- Comparative & International Education
- Educational Policy
- Families, Early Learning & Literacy
- Teaching, Learning & Teacher Development (including specially the teaching of mathmatics and sciences)

Oxford Brookes University
School of Education
Wheatley Campus
Wheatley
OXFORD   OX33 1HX

Tel: 01865 485930
Fax: 01865 485838
Email:
Website: www.brookes.ac.uk/schools/education

Contact Person: Linda Grace, Academic Administrator

Directions: Road: From Oxford, take A40 towards London. After ca. 3 miles, take turn-off for Wheatley. Through Wheatley village, after ca. 1 mile turn left and follow signs for Brookes University to the Wheatley Campus. The School of Education is sited in the tower block. From London, take M40 towards Oxford. Exit at Junction 8 and follow signs to Wheatley. From Wheatley, follow signs for Brookes University. Rail: Oxford; 40 minutes by taxi.

Staff: Head of School: Simon Catling
         Professors: 3
         Other teaching staff: 27 f/t; 13p/t
         Research staff & students: 2

Overall FTE students in 1999/2000: 1051

COURSES

ITE Primary: 1-year PGCE (69); 3-year BA QTS (76).
ITE Secondary: 1-year PGCE (108) in Maths, MFL, Music, Science, Geography, IT.
ITE Post-Compulsory: 1-year f/t Certificate in Education or PGCE (Post-Compulsory Education); 4-term p/t Certificate in Education or PGCE (Post-Compulsory Education).
CPD / Higher Degrees: 1-year f/t, 2-year p/t MA; 2-year p/t distance learning MA for Teachers in International Schools; 1-year f/t, 2-year p/t MA in Education by Open Learning; 2-year p/t Postgraduate Diploma in Educational Studies (Medical Needs); 1-year Certificate in Educational Studies (SEN); 2/3-year p/t BA (Professional Studies in Education); 1-year f/t or p/t Postgraduate Diploma in Educational Studies; 2-year p/t Postgraduate Diploma

in Education Studies; 2-year p/t Postgraduate Diploma in Education Studies (Hearing Impairment); 2-year p/t MSc (Audiology); 2-term p/t Certificate in Professional Studies in Education; 4-term Certificate in Education or PGCE (Post-Compulsory Education); 3-year f/t, 4-years p/t Doctorate in Education; f/t or p/t MPhil and PhD degrees by research.

Other Courses: 3-year BA Educational Studies; 2-term p/t Returning to Teaching course; other short courses.

PARTNERSHIPS

- The CatchUp Project: Designed to help children aged 7-8 years who are struggling with reading. It is a structured approach which takes place at the start of KS2 as part of regular weekly classroom practice and includes a ten- minute individual session, plus a 15 minute group reading session.
- Oxfordshire LEA-RADOX: A collaborative project on educational needs in Oxfordshire.
- Education Consortium: A consortium of Oxfordshire and Buckinghamshire LEAs, Westminster College, Oxford University Department of Education Studies and Oxford Brookes School of Education, to provide CPD opportunities for teachers in the region.
- OCTTIS: Oxfordshire Consortium for Teacher Training in Schools.

MAIN RESEARCH AND DEVELOPMENT INTERESTS

- Curriculum Development
- Teacher Education
- Special Education Needs
- Education Management
- Post-Compulsory Education
- Education & Development
- Educational Policy

OTHER SPECIAL FEATURES

- National Education Assessment Centre: A joint venture with Secondary Heads Association located within the School of Education.
- Oxford Centre for Education Management & Services: Responsible for management and other professional development courses and services.
- Consultancy and educational development for UNICEF, ODA, World Bank, British Council in South Asia and Southern and Central Africa, Eastern Europe, South America, Malaysia.

University of Plymouth
Rolle School of Education
Faculty of Arts & Education
Douglas Avenue
EXMOUTH EX8 2AT

Tel: 01395 255319
Fax: 01395 255303
Email: gmpayne@plymouth.ac.uk
Website: www.plym.ac.uk

Contact Person: Mrs Gillian Payne, Head of School

Directions: Road: Exit M5 at the Exeter turn-off. Take A376 to Exmouth (6 miles). In town, turn left at first set of traffic lights; on to mini-roundabout; turn right; at next mini-roundabout, turn left up hill; at top, turn right at next mini-roundabout; at next roundabout, turn left and follow road round to main entrance to campus. Rail: Exeter. Regular trains from Exeter to Exmouth (30 minutes).

Staff:
Head of School:	Mrs Gillian Payne	
Teaching staff:	44 f/t; 20 p/t	(total FAE: 106 f/t; 75 p/t)
Research staff:	13	

Overall FTE students in 1999/2000: 2500 (FAE)

COURSES

ITE Primary: BEd (160); PGCE (65)
ITE Secondary: PGCE (68) in Art & Design, Maths, Music, Geography, English.
ITE Post-Compulsory: PGCE Post-Compulsory Education & Training; BA Education & Training.
CPD / Higher Degrees: Linked modular award programme: Certificate in Professional Studies in Education (CPSE), Certificate of Advanced Professional Studies (CAPS), Postgraduate Certificate (PGCert), PGDip(Ed), MEd; Certificate in Education primarily for FE); MPhil; PhD; range of other courses and events offered across the region.

PARTNERSHIPS

Training partnerships for ITT have been established with primary schools across the South West, including nursery, first, middle and primary schools. Their locations are mainly in Devon, with a significant number also in Somerset and Dorset. There are also training partnerships with Finland and the USA. Training partnerships for the secondary programme are in Devon and Cornwall, with two levels identified as Partnership Schools and Mentor Schools. The School of Graduate Studies in Arts & Education has established partnerships with seven of the LEAs in the South West (Devon, Somerset, Dorset, Cornwall, Bournemouth, Torbay, Plymouth). In addition, there are partnerships with many individual schools.

MAIN RESEARCH AND DEVELOPMENT INTERESTS

- Teacher Education
- Religious, Moral & Cultural Education
- The Arts in Primary Education
- Language in Education
- Early Childhood Studies
- Mathematics Education
- Special Educational Needs

OTHER SPECIAL FEATURES

- Diploma and BA in Steiner (Waldorf) Education
- Early Childhood Studies as 'Main Subject' Area in BEd
- Education as Minor Pathway in BA (Combined Arts)
- Specialist Teacher Assistants Programmes
- Range of ten specialist subjects in BEd
- Flexible, modular approach at all levels with opportunities for APEL

University of Portsmouth
School of Education & Continuing Studies
St George's Building
141 High Street
PORTSMOUTH PO1 2HY

Tel: 023 9284 5300
Fax: 023 9284 5200
Email: secs.shsc.enquiries@port.ac.uk
Website: www.hum.port.ac.uk

Contact Person: Mr Mike Coeshott, Head of School

Directions: Road: M275 towards Portsmouth City centre, then follow signs to Isle of Wight ferry. The building ison the corner of High Street and St George's Road. Rail: Portsmouth Harbour; 10 minutes walk.

Staff: Head of School: Mr Mike Coeshott
            Teaching staff: 7 f/t; 12 p/t

Overall FTE students in 1999/2000: 366

COURSES

ITE Secondary: PGCE English, Maths, Science, MFL, Geography.
CPD / Higher Degrees: CertEd; PGCE Post-Compulsory; MSc Education & Training Management; MA Health Professional Education; MA Advanced Professional Practice in Education; BA Hons Professional & Continuing Education; BA Hons Ed.

PARTNERSHIPS

The University works in partnership with about 30 schools across four LEAs.

MAIN RESEARCH AND DEVELOPMENT INTERESTS

*   Social Foundation of Education
*   Teacher Training
*   Geographical Education
*   Process Models of Curriculum
*   Evaluation Process
*   Reflective Practice
*   Key Skills

- Dyslexia & Learning Difficulties
- Creative Learning
- Science Education
- Development of Schools Partnerships
- Access/Widening Participation
- The changing role of academics in HE following expansion of participation rates

OTHER SPECIAL FEATURES

The School includes the Centre for Continuing Studies which offers Further Education to the community of Portsmouth and surrounding areas. The programme offers a wide range of courses for people of all ages, interests and abilities.

University of Reading
School of Education
Bulmershe Court, Earley
READING   RG6 1HY

Tel: 0118 931 8861
Fax: 0118 935 2080
Email: emscroll@reading.ac.uk
Website: www.rdg.ac.uk

Contact Person: Professor Paul Croll, Head of School

Directions: Road: M4 / Exit 10 from the east, Exit 11 from the west. Bulmershe Court is one mile north of Reading University Whiteknights Campus (full details available on request). Rail: Reading; 15 minutes by taxi.

Staff: | Head of School: | Professor Paul Croll |
|---|---|
| Professors: | 8 |
| Other teaching staff: | 60 f/t; 20 p/t |
| Research staff & students: | 6; 70 |

Overall FTE students in 1999/2000: 830

COURSES

ITE Primary: 4-year BA(Ed) Hons (110) in Art, English, Geography & Environment, History, Maths, Music, Science, Technology; 1-year PGCE (30) with Early Years, Later Years and a taught Music specialism.

ITE Secondary: 1-year PGCE (250) Art & Design, Drama, English, Geography, History, Maths, MFL, Music, PE, Sciences; 2-year French Conversion course.

CPD / Higher Degrees: Modular MA/MSc and PG Diploma Programme with courses in: English & Language in Education, Managing School Improvement, Music Education, Primary Education, Inclusive Education; f/t or p/t MA/MSc courses in: IT in Education, Organisation/Planning/Management in Education, Mathematical Education for Development, Science Education for Development; Comparative Higher Education; MPhil and PhD by research, including a doctoral research methods programme.

Other Courses: Certificate in Education (FE); Certificate and Diploma in Further Professional Studies by short course credit accumulation; BA (Theatre Arts, Education, Deaf Studies).

MAIN RESEARCH AND DEVELOPMENT INTERESTS

The research work of the School is organised through seven academic divisions, most of which also incorporate established research centres and active research groups (shown in parentheses):

- *The Arts Group* (International Centre for Research in Music Education, Environmental Education Research Group)
- *History, Geography and Physical Education*
- *International and Comparative Aspects of Education* (Centre for International Studies in Education, Management and Training; Higher Education Research Group)
- *Language, Literacy and Drama Education* (Centre for Languages, English and Media Education)
- *Mathematics Education*
- *Science Education* (Models in Science and Technology Research and Education Group)
- *Social and Organisational Aspects of Education* (School Leadership and Improvement Centre; Group for Research in Individual Differences)

OTHER SPECIAL FEATURES

The School runs an innovative undergraduate degree in Theatre Arts, Education and Deaf Studies, recruiting both deaf and hearing students and is developing a new undergraduate degree in Sports Leadership. The Diploma in Music Teaching in Private Practice offers a distance learning professional and academic qualification to music teachers working in a variety of settings. The School also offers a two-year inservice BA(Ed) in Education Management for headteachers from overseas.

RIPON & YORK

Ripon & York (A college affiliated to the University of Leeds)

York Campus:	**Lord Mayor's Walk**
	YORK YO31 7EX
Ripon Campus:	**College Road**
	RIPON HG4 2QX

Tel: 01904 656771
Fax: 01904 612512
Email: i.waghorn@ucrysj.ac.uk
Website: www.ucrysj.ac.uk

Contact Person: Mr Ian Waghorn, Assistant Registrar

Directions: *York Campus:* British Rail to York , then a 10 minutes walk or shot taxi ride. *Ripon Campus:* British Rail to York or Harrogate, then bus to Ripon. There is a College minibus service between the two campuses.

Staff: <u>Head of School:</u>   Mr Ron Smith
          <u>Professors:</u>   1
          <u>Other teaching staff:</u> 19 f/t

Overall FTE students in 1999/2000: 732

COURSES

ITE Primary: 1-year f/t PGCE, age 3-8/7-11 (85) (York); 16-month p/t PGCE, age 3-8/7-11 (40); 4-year BA/BSc Hons QTS, age 3-8/7-11 (141) in English, Maths, Theology & RE, French, Music (Ripon).

ITE KS 2/3:   4-year integrated BA/BSc Hons QTS, age 7-14 (28) in Environmental Science or D&T (York).

ITE Secondary: 1-year PGCE, age 11-18 (28) in D&T, Music, RE (York).

CPD / Higher Degrees: Certificate; Diploma; MA; a wide range of subject areas with a particular focus on SEN and Early Years; Returning to Primary teaching courses with a high success rate for subsequent employment; a range of short courses.

PARTNERSHIPS

There are 250 schools in the Primary partnership, spanning York, North Yorkshire, East Yorkshire, Stockton on Tees, Cleveland and Middlesbrough and 35 schools in the Secondary partnership. School Mentors are trained and work closely with Link Tutors from the University College. CPD partnerships exist throughout the same geographical area with specific partnership arrangements focusing on particular areas of development, e.g. certificate courses in Professional Practice in Learning Support, aimed at classroom support and teaching assistants, developed and delivered with East Riding and additionally a number of jointly organixed one-day conferences.

MAIN RESEARCH AND DEVELOPMENT INTERESTS

- Quality Issues in ITT Partnership
- The Role of Video Conferencing in Exposing Students to International Teacher Education Issues
- Links between Student Motivational Style and Behaviour Management
- Young children making meaning through drawing and modelling at home and in pre-school settings

OTHER SPECIAL FEATURES

ITT and CPD activities operate from both of the two main campuses, offering provision over a wide geographical area.

ROEHAMPTON

Roehampton Institute London
Faculty of Education
Grove House
Roehampton Lane
LONDON   SW15 5PJ

Tel: 0181 392 3073
Fax: 0181 392 3335
Email: r.allison@roehampton.ac.uk
Website: www.roehampton.ac.uk

Contact Person: Professor Ron Best, Dean

Directions: British Rail to Barnes Station or bus connections with Hammersmith and Putney Bridge Underground.

Staff: <u>Dean of Faculty:</u>   Ron Best
         <u>Professors:</u>   6
         <u>Other teaching staff:</u> 47 f/t; 18 p/t
         <u>Research staff:</u>   6

Overall FTE students in 1999/2000: 1678

COURSES

ITE Primary: 4-year BA QTS, age 4-8/7-11 (346); 1-year PGCE (194)
ITE Secondary: 1-year PGCE (228) in Maths, English, Science, MFL, D&T, Technology, History, Art, Music, RE.
CPD / Higher Degrees: Masters programmes in English, Language & Literacy in Education, Art, Craft & Design in Education, Primary & Early Childhood Education, Choral Education; Education Studies, Education Management; modular Professional Development Programme leading to Certificates and Diplomas of Professional Practice (CPP, DPP); named certificates and diplomas; wide range of short courses and consultancy for schools.
Other Courses: 3-year single honours or joint honours BA Education with one or more of 21 other subjects (225).

PARTNERSHIPS

South West London Teacher Education Consortium (SWELTEC)

MAIN RESEARCH AND DEVELOPMENT INTERESTS

- Art Education
- Music Education
- Choral Education
- Education Management
- Science Education
- English Language & Literacy Education
- Educational Policy
- Pastoral Care, PSE & Spiritual Development
- Mathematics Education

OTHER SPECIAL FEATURES

Roehampton Institute London, an Institute of the University of Surrey, is a unique federation of four colleges founded by the Anglican, Methodist and Roman Catholic Churches and the Incorporated Froebel Educational Institute.

ST MARTIN'S

St Martin's College
Bowerham Road
Bowerham
LANCASTER   LA1 3JD

Tel: 01524 384384
Fax: 01524 384385
Email: k.jacques@ucsm.ac.uk
Website: www.ucsm.ac.uk

Contact Person: Kath Leigh

Directions: *on request*

Staff: Head of Department: Kate Jacques
          Professors: 2
          Other teaching staff: 40 f/t; 12 p/t
          Research staff: 2

Overall FTE students in 1999/2000: 2200 (in ITE)

COURSES

ITE Primary: 4-year BA/BSc QTS in Art & Design, D&T, Biology, English, Geography, History, Maths, Music, PE, Religious Studies, Drama; 3-year BA QTS Generalist; 1-year PGCE, age 3-8/7-12.
ITE KS 2/3:   4-year BA/BSc, age 7-14 in English, MFL, IT.
ITE Secondary: 1-year PGCE in Maths, Science, MFL, RE, Art, English, Geography, History, PE; 2-year BSc QTS in Maths, Science; 2-year PGCE in Maths, Science.
CPD / Higher Degrees: Certificate; MA; MPhil; PhD; extensive range of short courses.

PARTNERSHIPS

Extensive partnerships with schools in Lancashire, Cumbria, Blackburn, Blackpool and London. Through the Education Development Unit partnership and consultancy offered throughout the country.

MAIN RESEARCH AND DEVELOPMENT INTERESTS

- Educational Policy
- Urban Education
- Undergraduate Degrees as Preparation for Teaching
- Partnership

OTHER SPECIAL FEATURES

Education courses are delivered on the three main campuses of the University College at Ambleside, Lancaster and Carlisle. Extensive work is done in East London through the Urban Learning Foundation.

SCARBOROUGH

University College Scarborough
Filey Road
SCARBOROUGH   YO11 3AZ

Tel: 01723 362392
Fax: 01723 370815
Email: moyrab@ucscarb.ac.uk
Website: www.ucscarb.ac.uk

Contact Person: Ms Moyra Bentley

Directions: Road: From the West: M62 to Hull, then A614/165 (coastal route) or M62 leaving at Junction 37 (Howden), then follow to Scarborough/ Bridlington A163, B1249 and A64 into Scarborough. Rail: Regular Inter-City trains run from London, Newcastle and Edinburgh (change at York) and cross-country services from Liverpool/Manchester. Coast Line links Hull with Scarborough.

Staff: Head of School: Ms Moyra Bentley
              Teaching staff: 12 f/t; 6 p/t

Overall FTE students in 1999/2000: 220

COURSES

ITE Primary: 1-year PGCE (57), age 3-8; 3-year UG QTS, age 3/5-11 with specialisms in English, Maths, Science, ICT.
CPD / Higher Degrees: Certificate; MA in Primary Education; MA in Religious Studies; MA in Early Years Education.

PARTNERSHIPS

Strong partnerships exist with schools in North Yorkshire, Middlesborough, Redcar and Cleveland, East Yorkshire and Hull.

MAIN RESEARCH AND DEVELOPMENT INTERESTS

* Early Years Education
* Primary Children Learning Science
* ICT
* Behaviour Management
* Primary English

128

SHEFFIELD

University of Sheffield
Department of Educational Studies
The Education Building
388 Glossop Road
SHEFFIELD   S10 2JA

Tel: 0114 222 8087
Fax: 0114 279 6236
Email: education@sheffield.ac.uk
Website: www.shef.ac.uk/uni/academic/D-H/edu/

Contact Person: Mrs Mary Lou Hughes, Departmental Administration

Directions: Road: Exit 33 from M1. Follow Sheffield signs, then at first roundabout pick up signs to University. Rail: Sheffield; 10 minutes by taxi.

Staff: Head of Department: Professor Wilfred Carr
             Teaching staff: 36 f/t; 7 p/t
             Research staff/students: 4/168

Overall FTE students in 1999/2000: 664

COURSES

ITE Secondary: 1-year PGCE (180) in English, Geography, History, Maths, MFL (French, German, Russian, Spanish), Balanced Science.

CPD / Higher Degrees: Modular MEd or Diploma programmes in Educational Studies; f/t or p/t MA in Creative Writing for Film and Television; MSc in Educational Psychology; p/t MA in Post-16 Education & Training Policy; MEd for University Staff; distance learning MEds in Educational Studies, Educational Management, English Language Teaching (TESOL), Inclusive Education, Literacy, Science Education; Networked Collaborative Learning; distance learning MA in Early Childhood Education; f/t or p/t MPhil, EdD, PhD; Inservice Certificate in Education, Specific Learning Difficulties (Dyslexia); Sheffield Teachers Action Research Inservice Certificate in Education (Special & Inclusive Education, ICT in Education, 14-19 Education, Literacy, Early Childhood Education).

PARTNERSHIPS

The Department has long-established partnerships with its local LEAs so as to deliver ITE and TTA INSET courses. It works in close collaboration with 35 partnership schools in Sheffield and surrounding education authorities. The PGCE course is structured and planned on the basis of a strong three-way partnership between university tutors, teachers in partnership schools and students. TTA INSET is designed and delivered in partnership with three LEAs. The Department also has a number of overseas teaching links with governments and organisations in Dubai, Hong Kong, Singapore and Trinidad & Tobago.

MAIN RESEARCH AND DEVELOPMENT INTERESTS

- Curriculum & Pedagogy
- Higher Education
- Literacy
- Education Policy Innovation & Change
- Post-Compulsory Education & Training
- Inclusive Education

SHEFFIELD HALLAM

Sheffield Hallam University
School of Education
Collegiate Crescent Campus
SHEFFIELD S10 2BP

Tel: 0114 253 2306
Fax: 0114 253 2330
Email:
Website: www.shu.ac.uk

Contact Person:

Directions: Collegiate Crescent Campus is ca. 1.5 miles from the City Centre on Clarkenhouse Road, near the Hallamshire Hospital. Rail: Sheffield Midland; 15 minutes by taxi.

Staff: Head of School: Professor Di Bentley

No current information submitted for this edition. Please contact Sheffield Hallam University directly or refer to their website.

SOUTH BANK

South Bank University
Division of Education
Faculty of Humanities & Social Studies
103 Borough Road
LONDON   SE1 0AA

Tel: 0171 928 8989
Fax: 0171 815 5799
Email: lermans@sbu.ac.uk
Website: www.sbu.ac.uk

Contact Person: Pam Ray

Directions: Underground: Elephant & Castle (Northern and Bakerloo Lines), Waterloo (Northern and Bakerloo Lines), Borough (Northern Line). Rail: London Bridge (20 minutes walk or short bus ride), Waterloo, Waterloo East (bus to St George's Circus, then 5 minutes walk), Elephant & Castle. Bus: Numbers 344, 12, 35, 40, 45A, 68, 68A, 133, 171, P3.

Staff: Head of Division: Mr Hugh Baldry

No current information submitted for this edition. Please contact South Bank University directly or refer to their website.

University of Southampton
Research & Graduate School of Education
SOUTHAMPTON   SO17 1BJ

Tel: 01703 593475
Fax: 01703 593556
Email: educfac@soton.ac.uk
Website: www.soton.ac.uk/~educate/

Contact Person: Ms Ann Laver

Directions: Road: Enter Southampton on A33 from Winchester, turn left at third traffic lights (Burgess Road), right at second traffic lights (University Road), enter University left immediately after pedestrian traffic lights. The School of Education (Building 34) is second building on the left, opposite administration block. Rail: Southampton Parkway (1 hour from Waterloo); 15 minutes by taxi.

Staff: Head of Department: Professor Christopher Brumfit
            Professors: 6
            Other teaching staff: 26 f/t
            Research staff & students: 4

Overall FTE students in 1999/2000: 525

COURSES

ITE Primary: 1-year PGCE (75); General Primary with specialism in English, Mathematics or Science.
ITE Secondary: 1-year PGCE (206) in Maths, English, Physics, Chemistry, Biology, Geography, MFL, PE, IT, Music.
ITE Post-Compulsory: Certificate in Education (FE/HE) (200); BA in Post-Compulsory Education (60). These courses are franchised to eight regional Centres.
CPD / Higher Degrees: 1-year f/t, 2-year p/t specialist Diploma/MA(Ed) programmes in Adult and FE, Multicultural Education, Health Education, Language in Education, Management, PE, Science & Technology Education, Environmental Education; 1-year f/t MSc(Ed) programmes in Biology Education, Chemistry Education, Geographical Education, Physics Education; Certificates in Advanced Educational Studies in various fields; 1-year f/t or 2-year p/t MA in Applied Linguistics for language teaching; 1-year f/t, 2-year p/t MSc programmes in Health Education/Health Promotion, Computer-based

Learning & Training; MPhil; PhD; MPhil Research Methodology (ESRC recognition); EdD; a variety of short courses, Research Training mode A recognised by ESRC.

PARTNERSHIPS

46 secondary schools; 64 primary schools; 8 FE and HE institutions.

MAIN RESEARCH AND DEVELOPMENT INTERESTS

- Education Marketing
- Environmental Education
- Health Education
- Language in Education
- Management in Education
- Multicultural Education
- Science, Mathematics, Geography, Technology & Physical Education
- Media Education
- Auto/Biography in Education
- Applied Linguistics in Education
- Foreign Language Learning
- Primary Education
- FE and HE

OTHER SPECIAL FEATURES

- Centres for Mathematics Education (with Faculty of Mathematical Studies) and Language in Education (with Faculty of Arts)
- Centre for Research in Education Marketing
- Centre for Biography & Education
- Media Education Centre
- Joint activities with King Alfred's College of HE (accredited)
- Contributor to Regional Credit Transfer Scheme

Stranmillis University College
A College of The Queen's University of Belfast
Stranmillis Road
BELFAST   BT9 5DY

Tel: 02890 381271
Fax: 02890 664423
Email: principal@stran-ni.ac.uk *or* registry@stran-ni.ac.uk
Website: www.stran-ni.ac.uk

Contact Person: Principal's Secretary

Directions: On bus route from city centre, located in the south of the city, ten minutes walk from The Queen's University.

Staff: Principal: Professor Richard McMinn
             Professors: 1
             Other teaching staff: 58 f/t; 4 p/t
             Research staff: 1

Overall FTE students in 1999/2000: 891 (ITE and CPD only)

COURSES

ITE Primary: 4-year BEd (150), age 4-11
ITE Secondary: 4-year BEd (45), age 11-18
CPD / Higher Degrees: CertProfDev; AdvCertEd; DASE; MEd; MSc.
Other Courses: 1-year PGCE (Educational Psychology) (15); TESOL Cert.

PARTNERSHIPS

Non-contractual partnerships with schools and further education colleges for ITT. Informal partnerships with Education and Library Boards in relation to Induction and Early Professional Development.

MAIN RESEARCH AND DEVELOPMENT INTERESTS

* Early Years Education
* Child Development
* Disaffection in a NI Context
* Selection at Age Eleven in a NI Context
* Effective Schooling and School Improvement

- Underachievement in a NI Context
- Disadvantage in a NI Context
- Values Education in a NI Context
- Education for Citizenship in a NI Context
- Teacher Education

OTHER SPECIAL FEATURES

The College offers a BA (Early Childhood Studies), which does not carry QTS, on both a part-time and a full-time basis, along with a number of other degree programmes, unrelated to teacher education, at both under-graduate and postgraduate levels. It has strong links with partner institutions in the European Union through staff exchanges and through the ERASMUS student exchange programme (20% of all BEd Students). The College has a major involvement in Education for Mutual Understanding programmes within the NI context.

SUNDERLAND

University of Sunderland
School of Education
Hammerton Hall
Gray Road
SUNDERLAND   SR2 8JB

Tel: 0191 515 2395
Fax: 0191 515 2629
Email: helen.chambers@sunderland.ac.uk
Website: www.sund.ac.uk

Contact Person:

Directions: Gray Road is off Ryhope Road, just south of Sunderland Civic Centre.

Staff: <u>Head of School:</u> Professor George Shield

COURSES

ITE Primary: 4-year BA(Hons) Early Years Education, age 3-8; 4-year BA(Hons) Junior Years Education, age 7-11.
ITE KS 2/3: 3-year BA(Hons) IT Education; 2-year BA(Hons) Middle Years Education (D&T, Maths, Science).
ITE Secondary: 4-year BA/BSc(Hons) D&T Education; 3-year BA(Hons) in English Education, IT Education, Geography Education, RE; 2-year BA/BSc(Hons) in D&T Education, IT Education, Music Education, Business Education, MFL Education (French, German, Spanish), Maths Education, Science Education; 1-year PGCE in Science, Maths, D&T, IT, Music, MFL, Geography, English, Business Studies.
ITE Post-Compulsory: CertEd.
CPD / Higher Degrees: MA, MPhil, PhD.

SURREY

University of Surrey
School of Educational Studies
GUILDFORD   GU2 5XH

Tel: 01483 300800
Fax: 01483 259519
Email: e.oliver@surrey.ac.uk
Website: www.surrey.ac.uk/education

Contact Person: Mrs Elizabeth Oliver

Directions: Road: From A3 take exit marked 'University Cathedral' (not Guildford). The Department is on the 4th floor, Senate House. Rail: Guildford; 5 minutes by taxi, 15 minutes walk from rear entrance of station, Link Bus from rear entrance to Senate House.

Staff: Head of School: Professor Stephen McNair
                Professors: 5
                Other teaching staff: 20 (Postgraduate Education)
                Research staff & students: 83

Overall FTE students in 1999/2000: 295 (Postgraduate Education and Research)

COURSES

ITE Post-Compulsory: PGCEA
CPD / Higher Degrees: MPhil; PhD; EdD; MSc/PG Diploma/PG Certificate in Applied Professional Studies in Education and Training, Counselling and Psychotherapy as a Means to Health, Management Consultancy, Gerontology: Policy, Care and Practice; MSc in Change Agent Skills and Strategies, Research in Education.

PARTNERSHIPS

These are many and varied and include strong links with Europe, the School having participated in international/comparative projects since the mid-seventies.

MAIN RESEARCH AND DEVELOPMENT INTERESTS

Research is clustered around six major themes. All themes address aspects of lifelong learning in different and distinctive ways and all have regional, national and international dimensions:

- Adult Learning and Curriculum Development
- Policy Studies in Post-Compulsory Education / Education, Training and Development
- Policy and Change in Higher Education
- Change Management and Therapeutic Education
- Nursing and Midwifery Education
- Professional Development and Education

OTHER SPECIAL FEATURES

In their first year, all research students are offered a common research methods programme in both quantative and qualitative research methods. This aims to develop knowledge and skills and to provide support. The School is recognised by the Economic and Social Research Council (ESRC) as a Mode A outlet and applications can be made to them for full-time or part-time studentships.

The Centre has also received funds from the General Nursing Council Trust and the Council of the Midwife Teachers Training College to endow a chair in Education in Nursing and a Director of Midwifery Education Research.

SUSSEX

University of Sussex
Institute of Education
Education Development Building
Falmer
BRIGHTON   BN1 9RG

Tel: 01273 606755
Fax: 01273 678568
Email: g.carrell@sussex.ac.uk
Website: www.sussex.ac.uk/USIE

Contact Person: Professor Joan Bliss, Director of USIE

Directions: Located on the A27 between Brighton and Lewes. On entering the University campus, follow the road round to the left and down the hill. The Education Development Building is on Arts Road. Parking at the rear. British Rail: Falmer, 20 minute service from Brighton or Lewes.

Staff: Director of Institute: Professor Joan Bliss
Teaching staff: 19 f/t; 12 p/t
Research staff: 5

Overall FTE students in 1999/2000: 334

COURSES

ITE Secondary: 1-year PGCE (138) in English, Geography, History, Maths, Music (2-year p/t option available), MFL, Science.
CPD / Higher Degrees: MPhil/DPhil Education; Professional Doctorate (EdD); MPhil/DPhil Creative Writing; p/t modular MA in Education & Accreditation of CPD; f/t or p/t MA in Education (Independent Studies); p/t MA in Education (School Effectiveness); f/t and sandwich MA in International Education; p/t MA/Diploma in Public Service Management; p/t MA in SEN; p/t Diploma in Education.
Other Courses: P/t Diploma/Masters in Clinical Supervision; p/t Postgraduate Diploma in Counselling (taken within the Counselling & Psychotherapy Unit).

PARTNERSHIPS

- Sussex Consortium for Teacher Education involving East and West Sussex Brighton and Hove schools and LEAs.
- Advisory and Inspection Service, West Sussex
- Other links include:
  - The Institute of Development Studies (IDS)
  - SPRU Science & Technology Policy Research
  - University of Cambridge Local Examinations Syndicate
- Research and consultancy links in China, India, South East Asia, Africa, the Caribbean.

MAIN RESEARCH AND DEVELOPMENT INTERESTS

- International Education & Development
- Arts Education & Aesthetics
- Teacher Education
- Professional, Vocational & Continuing Education
- Learning, Teaching & Assessment

OTHER SPECIAL FEATURES

The University of Sussex Institute of Education comprises three vertical strands and the Centre for International Education which links into activities of the other three strands:

- The Research & Development Strand promotes a culture in which research flourishes through support for groups and individuals.
- The Graduate Research Centre in Education provides and enhances post-graduate teaching and research training programmes.
- The Sussex Consortium for Teacher Education focuses on ITE.

The Institute works with LEAs, institutions of FE, consortia or groups of schools, individual schools, etc. to design programmes to meet identified needs. The Institute also runs a Distance DPhil programme in collaboration with David Yellin Teachers' College, Israel.

SWANSEA INSTITUTE

Swansea Institute of Higher Education
Faculty of Humanities, Education & Health Care
Townhill Road
SWANSEA   SA2 0UT

Tel: 01792 481246
Fax: 01792 481256
Email: k.jones@sihe.ac.uk
Website: www.sihe.ac.uk

Contact Person: Miss Tania Bromham, Faculty Secretary

Directions: Swansea High Street Station

Staff: Dean of Faculty: Professor Kenneth L Jones
              Teaching staff: 30 f/t; 5 p/t

Overall FTE students in 1999/2000: 520

COURSES

ITE Primary: 3- and 4-year BA (Education) (100); General Primary, age 3-11 in English, Maths, Science, Humanities.
ITE Secondary: 1-year PGCE Business Studies (15); 4-year BA Business Education (15).
CPD / Higher Degrees: Extensive range of short accredited courses for schools; PGCE/Cert FE; modular MA Education specialising in primary curriculum and primary and secondary school management.

PARTNERSHIPS

The Institute is in full partnership with local primary and secondary schools and FE institutions as part of its ITT provision. There is a school-based purpose-designed MA Education focusing on school management. The Faculty works closely with adjacent LEAs and accredits much of local inservice provision.

MAIN RESEARCH AND DEVELOPMENT INTERESTS

* Development in Learning & Teaching
* Language & Literacy
* School Management & Improvement

OTHER SPECIAL FEATURES

- The ITT Primary BA Education course has a common foundation year after which students elect to follow either a further two years of study for a 3-year BA(Ed) Hons or a further three years of study for a 4-year BA(Ed)Hons.
- The 4-year BA(Ed) course has a module addressing the teaching of children with special educational needs.

TRINITY CARMARTHEN

Trinity College
College Road
CARMARTHEN SA31 3EP

Tel: 01267 676767
Fax: 01267 676766
Email:
Website: www.trinity-cm.ac.uk

Contact Person:

Directions: When approaching from the M4 take the second exit towards the West, carry on to the next roundabout and take the first exit. Travel for ca. a quarter of a mile and take first exit for Llanstephan. Turn left at junction on slip road and from there follow signs to Trinity College.

Staff: <u>Head of Department:</u> Dr Medwyn Hughes

No current information submitted for this edition. Please contact Trinity College directly or refer to their website.

TRINITY & ALL SAINTS

Trinity & All Saints College
Brownberrie Lane
Horsforth
LEEDS   LS18 5HD

Tel: 0113 283 7100
Fax: 0113 283 7200
Email: t.edwards@tasc.ac.uk
Website: www.tasc.ac.uk

Contact Person: Dr John Hill

Directions: *on request*

Staff: Dean of Faculty: Dr John Hill
             Teaching staff: 12 f/t; 11 p/t

Overall FTE students in 1999/2000: 679

COURSES

ITE Primary: 4-year BA/BSc QTS, age 5-11 (150).
ITE Secondary: 1-year PGCE, age 11-16/18 (175) in English, Maths, MFL (French, German, Spanish), RE, D&T (age 11-16), IT (age 11-16), Business Studies (age 14-19).
CPD / Higher Degrees: PhD; MEd; Diploma and Certificate courses in professional development and subject studies.

PARTNERSHIPS

ITE compacts exist with ca. 50 secondary and 120 primary schools in West Yorkshire and North Yorkshire LEAs and with independent schools.

MAIN RESEARCH AND DEVELOPMENT INTERESTS

- Catholic Education
- History Education
- Special Needs Education
- Assessment
- Physical Education
- Modern Languages Education

OTHER SPECIAL FEATURES

- Centre for History Education (Schools History Project)
- Comenius Centre (Centre for Information on Language Teaching and Research) - one of a national network of modern languages training and resource centres.

ULSTER

University of Ulster
School of Education, HQ
COLERAINE   BT52 1SA

Tel: 01265 44141
Fax: 01265 40918
Email:
Website: www.ulst.ac.uk

Contact Person:

Directions:

Staff: <u>Head of School:</u>   Professor Harry McMahon

No current information submitted for this edition. Please contact
University of Ulster directly or refer to their website.

WALES ABERYSTWYTH

University of Wales Aberystwyth
Department of Education
Old College, King Street
ABERYSTWYTH   SY23 2AX

Tel: 01970 622103/4
Fax: 01970 622258
Email: mbb@aber.ac.uk
Website: www.aber.ac.uk/~ednwww

Contact Person: Mrs Margaret Bevan, Department Administrator

Directions: The Education Department is situated in the Old College on the promenade, opposite the pier. Rail: Aberystwyth (trains from England via Birmingham).

Staff: Head of Department: Professor Richard Daugherty
            Professors: 3 (including HoD)
            Other teaching staff: 16 f/t; 15 p/t
            Research staff & students: 5 f/t; 10 p/t

Overall FTE students in 1999/2000: 350

COURSES

ITE Primary: 1-year PGCE, age 3-8/7-11 (127); Early Years/General Primary in English, Welsh, History, Geography, Maths, Music, PE, Science.
ITE Secondary: 1-year PGCE, age 11-18 (169) in English, Drama, Geography, History, MFL, Sciences, Welsh.
CPD / Higher Degrees: Certificate; Diploma; MEd; MPhil; PhD
Other Courses: Joint honours degree course in Education with a wide range of subjects.

PARTNERSHIPS

The PGCE Partnership for the training of secondary school teachers includes 40 schools, that for primary 110. The schools of the secondary partnership are scattered over most of Wales, the primary partnership extends into parts of Shropshire.

154

MAIN RESEARCH AND DEVELOPMENT INTERESTS

* Bilingualism
* Curriculum & Assessment
* Education Policy in Wales
* Ethnic Minorities
* Health Education
* Language and Learning
* Language & Gender
* Literacy
* Media & Education
* New Technology / ICT
* Small Schools

OTHER SPECIAL FEATURES

Most of the Department's courses are available in both English and Welsh, and supervision of research is available in either language. Attached to the Department is the Centre for Educational Studies which produces and publishes books and other teaching resources for Welsh-medium education.

WALES BANGOR

University of Wales Bangor
Faculty & School of Education
Normal Site, Holyhead Road
BANGOR   LL57 2PX

Tel: 01248 383001
Fax: 01248 383092
Email: eds011@bangor.ac.uk
Website: www.bangor.ac.uk

Contact Person: Mr Gwynfor ab Ifor, School Administrator

Directions: From roundabout where A5 and A55 converge, follow Holyhead signs to Ysbyty Gwynedd exit and turn left. At next roundabout follow Bangor signs on Treborth Road for ca. half a mile to Antelope roundabout and continue following Bangor signs. Normal Site is situated on left of road, overlooking Menai Straits.

Staff: Head of School: Dr H Gareth Ff Roberts
Professors: 2
Other teaching staff: 42 f/t; 7 p/t
Research staff & students: 6

Overall FTE students in 1999/2000: 738

COURSES

ITE Primary: 1-year PGCE, age 3-8/7-12 (63); 3-year BEd Hons QTS, age 3-12.

ITE Secondary: 1-year PGCE (211) in Outdoor Activities, French, German, Welsh, English, Maths, Science (Biology, Chemistry, Physics), IT, RE, PE, Music, Art; 3-year BEd Hons QTS in D&T.

CPD / Higher Degrees: Short courses in various centres in North Wales; 1-year f/t, 2-year p/t MA/MEd (or Diploma); modular p/t MA/MEd courses in SEN (including Dyslexia), Counselling, Further & Adult Education, Curriculum Studies, European Dimensions, Mentoring, Research Design, Management & Marketing of Education, Children's Literature & Mathematics; diploma course in SEN in Welsh.

Other Courses: Welsh medium Joint Honours courses in Education (Addysg) which combine with several subjects in the Faculty of Arts.

PARTNERSHIPS

Strong primary and secondary partnerships inform the continuous development of the School's range of courses. There are partnerships with 170 primary schools distributed across North Wales and parts of North West England and with 42 secondary schools covering North Wales.

MAIN RESEARCH AND DEVELOPMENT INTERESTS

- Bilingualism / Bilingual Education
- Welsh Language Teaching
- Standardisation of Welsh Technical Terminology
- Science & Technology Education
- IT in Education
- Mathematics Education
- Records of Achievement in HE
- The European Dimension in Education
- RE & Welsh Literacy / English Literacy in Welsh Schools

The School houses a wide range of developmental work including the piloting and administration of assessment material and the creation of Welsh-medium support materials across the curriculum at all Key Stages.

OTHER SPECIAL FEATURES

The School validates CFPS and other courses offered by local LEAs. It houses specialist centres for special needs, nursery education and assessment. The Welsh National Centre for RE is also based at the School.

All ITT courses in the School are available in both English and Welsh and corresponding teaching placements are available in Welsh-medium and English-medium schools. Students may also take the opportunity to learn Welsh.

WALES INSTITUTE

University of Wales Institute, Cardiff
School of Education
Cyncoed Campus
Cyncoed Road
CARDIFF   CF23 6XD

Tel: 01222 506461
Fax: 01222 506589
Email: degan@uwic.ac.uk
Website: www.uwic.ac.uk

Contact Person: Mr David Egan, Head of School

Directions: The Cyncoed Campus of UWIC is based in the north of the city of Cardiff. Being close to Eastern Avenue and the A470, both of which lead to the M4, it is easily accessible by private and public transport.

Staff: Head of School: Mr David Egan
             Teaching staff: 60 f/t
             Research staff: 3

Overall FTE students in 1999/2000: 1200

COURSES

ITE Primary: 1-year PGCE (100); 3-year BA Primary Education (140).
ITE Secondary: 1-year PGCE (290) in Art & Design, English, D&T, History, Maths, MFL, Music, Science, PE, Welsh; 2-year BA Education in Music (18), in Welsh (20); 4-year BA Education in Drama (30).
CPD / Higher Degrees: Modular p/t MA Education with pathways in primary, secondary, Post-Compulsory, art & design education; modular diploma courses in mentoring, media education, early years and in various aspects of physical education and sport; MPhil; PhD.
Other Courses: Access to Teacher Education (aimed at ethnic minority access to primary ITT).

PARTNERSHIPS

For ITT with 256 primary schools and 98 secondary schools in South East Wales. The partnership also extends to CPD links.

MAIN RESEARCH AND DEVELOPMENT INTERESTS

- Numeracy at Key Stages 1 and 2
- Literacy at Key Stages 1 and 2
- The Teaching of Welsh History in Schools
- The Teaching of Welsh
- School Inspection & School Improvement
- Open & Distance Learning Routes for PGCE Secondary
- Music Education
- Environmental & Development Education
- Welsh Education Policy & the National Assembly

OTHER SPECIAL FEATURES

Whilst educating and training ITT and CPD students for the context of England and Wales, the School of Education offers full opportunities for Welsh-medium education through provision of teaching opportunities (in college and in school) in the Welsh language. The Welsh dimension in education is also a strong feature of research and scholarly activity.

WALES SWANSEA

University of Wales Swansea
Department of Education
Hendrefoelan
SWANSEA SA2 7NB

Tel: 01792 295355 / 518682
Fax: 01792 290219
Email: h.z.powell@swansea.ac.uk
Website: www.swan.ac.uk/education

Contact Person: Department Administrator

Directions: Rail: Swansea; 10 minutes by taxi. Map available on request.

Staff: Head of Department: Professor Roy Lowe
Teaching staff: 14 f/t; 23 p/t

Overall FTE students in 1999/2000: 469

COURSES

ITE Primary: 1-year PGCE, age 3-8/7-11.
ITE Secondary: 1-year PGCE in Biology, Chemistry, D&T, English, Geography, History, Maths, MFL, Physics, Welsh, ICT.
CPD / Higher Degrees: Modular MA(Ed) in a wide range of areas offered with flexible modes of delivery including intensive weekend courses, distance learning and school-based research; inservice training programmes for teachers, head teachers, lecturers and administrators which offer a wide range of award-bearing and non award-bearing courses.

PARTNERSHIPS

The Department has well-established partnerships with a wide range of both Primary and Secondary schools in South Wales.

MAIN RESEARCH AND DEVELOPMENT INTERESTS

* Curriculum
* Teacher Education
* Mathematics Education
* Policy & History Studies
* Use of ICT in Schools

- Development of New Delivery Strategies in ITE
- Boys' and Girls' Achievement in Schools
- Mentoring in ITE
- Changing Strategies in Educational Research

OTHER SPECIAL FEATURES

The Department has an outreach Masters programme in Athens and has developed an EdD programme which is due to start in January 2000.

WARWICK

University of Warwick
Institute of Education and Department of Continuing Education
COVENTRY CV4 7AL

Tel: 02476 523523
Fax: 02476 524177
Email: j.coleman@warwick.ac.uk
Website: www.warwick.ac.uk/wie

Contact Person: Jane Coleman, Administrator

Directions: Road: The University is some 3 miles south of the centre of Coventry and 3 miles north of Kenilworth in the angle of the A45 and A429. Follow road signs to University, then institutional signs to Westwood where departments and institutes are individually signposted. Rail: Coventry; 10 minutes by taxi.

Staff:

Head of Department:	Professor Jim Campbell
Professors:	8
Teaching staff:	65 f/t; 45 p/t
Research staff & students:	100

Overall FTE students in 1999/2000: 1100

COURSES

ITE Primary: 1-year PGCE (47); 4-year BA Hons QTS in English, Maths, Science, Art, Music, Drama (127).

ITE Secondary: 1-year PGCE (354) in Economics with Business Studies, English, Maths, MFL, Science, IT, RE.

CPD / Higher Degrees: Modular units allowing for combination of f/t and p/t study leading to postgraduate certificates, diplomas and masters awards; 2-year f/t BEd for overseas teachers; 2-year and 4-year f/t BA Hons in TESOL; annual short course programmes for teachers; research degrees (MA, MPhil, PhD); 4-year p/t taught EdD; MA degrees in Educational Studies, Educational Management, Arts Education and Cultural Studies, Art & Design Education, Religious Education, Drama Education, Music Education, Children's Literature Studies; MSc in Mathematics or Science Education; MA in Continuing Education.

PARTNERSHIPS

The Institute is currently in partnership with ca. 180 primary and 65 secondary schools for the Initial Teacher Training of BA QTS and PGCE students. The majority of the schools are in the LEAs of Coventry, Solihull and Warwickshire, but we also have partner schools in Leicestershire, Birmingham, Staffordshire, Northamptonshire and Worcestershire. Amongst other developments, we are introducing an intranet link between the University and partner schools to improve communication. The Institute's CPD partnership extends to the local authorities in the region, to the development of the Virtual Staff College and a range of other activities, particularly in the field of ICT.

MAIN RESEARCH AND DEVELOPMENT INTERESTS

A wide range of research reflecting interests of academic staff as well as research based in specialised centres and units:
- Centre for Educational Development, Appraisal & Research
- Centre for Education & Industry
- Mathematics Education Research Centre
- Centre for Research in Elementary & Primary Education
- Centre for English Language Teacher Education
- Centre for New Technologies and Research in Education
- Psychology & Special Needs Research Unit
- Teacher Development Unit
- Warwick Religions & Education Research Unit
- Unit for Research in Education, Cultures & the Arts
- Environmental Sciences Research & Education Unit

OTHER SPECIAL FEATURES

The Department of Continuing Education runs the University's p/t degree, 2+2 degrees and Open Studies programmes. There are close links through course development and validation with FE institutions in the region. The University also houses a centre for the National Professional Qualification for Headship.

WEST OF ENGLAND

University of the West of England
Faculty of Education
Redland Campus
Redland Hill
BRISTOL BS6 6UZ

Tel: 0117 974 1251
Fax: 0117 976 2146
Email:
Website: www.uwe.ac.uk

Contact Person: Suzanne Maxwell, Faculty Administrator

Directions: Road: Junction 19 from M4 to M32; Junction 2 from M32. Detailed directions from M32 are available on request. Rail: Bristol Temple Meads; 15 minutes by taxi.

Staff: Dean of Faculty: Professor Kate Ashcroft
              Teaching staff: 52

Overall FTE students in 1999/2000: 1100

COURSES

ITE Primary: 4-year BA/BSc Hons QTS, age 5-8/7-11, in Art, Biology, English, Geography, History, Maths; Advanced Early Years Study, age 3-8; 1-year PGCE, age 3-8/7-11, General Primary with specialism in National Curriculum subject; Advanced Early Years Study, age 3-8.

ITE Secondary: 1-year PGCE in Art, Biology, Business Education, D&T, English, Geography, History, Maths, MFL.

CPD / Higher Degrees: Postgraduate Certificate/Diploma; MA Education; EdD; MPhil; PhD; other postgraduate awards leading to qualifications in: General, SEN, FE/HE/Adult Education, Education Management, Guidance (Vocational/Educational), Careers Guidance, Raising Achievement in City Schools.

PARTNERSHIPS

The Faculty works with its partner schools and colleges to offer students a balance of school and higher education experience. It fosters these relationships in course design and delivery and responsibility is shared for the development and assessment of trainees' standards. Partnership is extended beyond initial training to induction support and appropriate professional development.

MAIN RESEARCH AND DEVELOPMENT INTERESTS

The Faculty has a long established expertise in research which
* adds to theoretical knowledge
* adds to knowledge about current practice
* supports the development of practice

These research groups, each led by a senior researcher, stimulate and support research in specific areas:
* Inclusivity and SEN
* Professional Education Research
* Teaching and Learning Research
* Programme & Policy Evaluation

Examples of current research:
* Towards Effective Learning in a Secondary School
* Special School in Special Measures - the Role of Action Planning
* Competence-based Assessment Systems
* Teaching History in Primary Schools
* The ARKive Multimedia Resource on Endangered Species

WESTMINSTER

Westminster College
Harcourt Hill
OXFORD OX2 9AT

Tel: 01865 247644
Fax: 01865 251847
Email: l.rowe@ox-west.ac.uk
Website: www.ox-west.ac.uk

Contact Person: Ms Linda Rowe

Directions: Road: *A34 going north:* Between Hinksey and Botley inter-changes take exit signposted Westminster College; left turn up Harcourt Hill; College on right at top of hill. *A34 going south:* Exit at Botley interchange; first exit from roundabout signposted Oxford; turn right into Westway, then into Westminster Way at traffic lights under road bridge; continue straight (do not bear left back on to the A34) into Harcourt Hill.

Staff: Head of School: Dr David Langford
Teaching staff: 32 f/t; 16 p/t
Research staff: 3

Overall FTE students in 1999/2000: 1090

COURSES

ITE Primary: 1-year PGCE, age 3-8/7-11 (72); 4-year BEd KS1/2 (106).
ITE KS 2/3: 4-year BEd (with French) (15).
ITE Secondary: 1-year PGCE (145) in Art, English, MFL, RE; 1-year PGCE Maitrise.
CPD / Higher Degrees: MEd/Dip Ed: The Management of Evidence-based Innovation and Change; BPhil and Certificates: Individual Differences (Special Needs and Able Children), Challenging Behaviour, ICT in Education and Training, Curriculum Design for Lifelong Learning, Learning in the Early Years, Education for Citizenship and Personal and Social Development, Research Design; MPhil / PhD.

PARTNERSHIPS

The College has been developing its partnership with schools using an 'internship' model, especially in the secondary phase. Trained mentors work in partnership with College tutors to enable support and assess student teachers' progress. The continuing evolution of the Partnership is overseen by Partnership committees with a membership which comprises a majority of teachers.

Other key partnerships:

- With Buckinghamshire LEA to promote research and developments in school self-evaluation alongside the development of CPD through support for school CPD Co-ordinators.
- With Swindon to development community-based initiatives in Lifelong Learning and CPD opportunities for all who work in schools.
- Consortium with Oxford University, Brookes University, Buckinghamshire and Oxfordshire LEAs to support and develop targeted CPD.

MAIN RESEARCH AND DEVELOPMENT INTERESTS

- Able Children
- Special Educational Needs
- Citizenship
- RE & Personal Development
- Learning Patterns & Profiles among Adult Learners
- Career Development Profiles for Teachers

The College also houses the National Primary Centre and the National Association for Able Children in Education.

OTHER SPECIAL FEATURES

The College specialises in teacher education and the humanities. The PGCE, BEd and MEd degrees are awarded by the University of Oxford creating a special link with the University and giving students access to lectures, the Bodleian Library and to the Oxford Union. There are international exchange agreements with universities in, for example, the USA, Canada, Belgium and France.

In August 2000 Westminster College will merge with the School of Education at Oxford Brookes University to form the university's new Westminster Institute of Education.

WOLVERHAMPTON

University of Wolverhampton
School of Education
Gorway Road
WALSALL   WS1 3BD

Tel: 01902 321050
Fax: 01902 323177
Email: sed-enquiries@wlv.ac.uk
Website: www.wlv.ac.uk/education

Contact Person: Hugh Somervell, Admissions Coordinator

Directions: Road: Leave M6 at Junction 7, follow A34 to Walsall. After 2 miles cross A4148 (Walsall Ring Road) at double mini-roundabout. Take next left into Jesson Road and left again into Gorway Road (follow signs for University). Bus no 51 from Birmingham or Walsall.

Staff: Dean of School: Sir Geoff Hampton

No current information submitted for this edition. Please contact University of Wolverhampton directly or refer to their website.

WOLVERHAMPTON

WORCESTER

University College Worcester
Faculty of Education & Psychology
Henwick Grove
WORCESTER WR2 6AJ

Tel: 01905 855000
Fax: 01905 855132
Email: h.emery@worc.ac.uk
Website: www.worc.ac.uk

Contact Person: Dr Hilary Emery, Dean of Faculty

Directions: Road: Signposted from Junction 7, M5. Rail: Worcester Foregate Street Station; then taxi.

Staff: Head of ITE Department: Mr Chris Oulton
Professors: 2
Other teaching staff: 67 f/t, 19 p/t
Research staff/students: 9/51

Overall FTE students in 1999/2000: 1492

COURSES

ITE Primary: 1-year PGCE, age 3-8/7-11 (80) in Advanced Early Years, English, ICT, Maths, Science; 3-year BA QTS Professional, age 3-8/7-11 (59) in Advanced Early Years, English, ICT, Maths, Science; 4-year BA QTS Subject/Professional, age 3-8/7-11 (48) in Art, English, Science, PE.

ITE KS 2/3: 4-year BA QTS Subject/Professional (14), age 7-14 in PE.

ITE Secondary: 1-year PGCE (182) in Business & Economics, D&T (Food & Textiles), English, Geography, History, Maths, MFL (French, German), Music, PE, Science.

CPD / Higher Degrees: Modular framework with a range of professional certificates/diplomas; BA(Ed) Inservice; Postgraduate Certificates, Diplomas, MA/MSc in SEN, Early Childhood Education, School Improvement & Management, Reflective Practice; special courses for Returning Teachers, Specialist Teaching Assistants; intensive courses for non-UK teachers; MPhil; PhD.

Other Courses: Educational Studies (42) as a subject on the Undergraduate Modular Scheme; Early Childhood HND/Degree (75); Graduate and Registered Teacher Programme.

PARTNERSHIPS

All ITE operates in partnership with schools in Worcestershire, Hereford-
shire and other neighbouring authorities. The College has signed a memoran-
dum of agreement with Worcestershire LEA and is developing specialist partnerships with individual schools.

On CPD the College works in partnership with Worcestershire, Hereford-
shire, Staffordshire, Warwickshire, Coventry, Birmingham and Solihull CBC.

MAIN RESEARCH AND DEVELOPMENT INTERESTS

- Early Years
- Learning & Teaching in schools / the workplace / HE
- Special Needs
- Assessment & Testing
- Environmental Education
- Institutional Development & Policy
- Information Technology Development
- Early Years Mathematics
- International Developments
- Psychology-related Interest
- Impact of CPD on Practice

The Faculty supports four research centres:

- Children's Literature & Literacy
- Early Childhood
- Policy into Practice
- Special Needs

YORK

University of York
Department of Educational Studies
Heslington
YORK   YO10 5DD

Tel: 01904 433453
Fax: 01904 433459
Email: educ15@york.ac.uk
Website: www.york.ac.uk

Contact Person: Dr Bob Campbell

Directions: Road: The university is marked on exits from the A64. The Department of Educational Studies is located on the main campus in Langwith College. Rail: York (on the east coast route); 15 minutes by taxi; there is also an excellent bus service. Journey time from London is 2 hours.

Staff: Head of Department: Dr Bob Campbell
              Professors: 3
              Teaching staff: 15 f/t; 4 p/t
              Research staff/students: 3/35

Overall FTE students in 1999/2000: 340

COURSES

ITE Secondary: 1-year PGCE (146) in English, History, Maths, MFL, Science.

CPD / Higher Degrees: Diploma in Applied Educational Studies; MA in Educational Studies; MA in Applied Educational Studies; MA in Primary Education; MA in Science Education; MA in Education (by research); MPhil; DPhil.

Other Courses: BA in Educational Studies (non QTS); BA/BSc in Educational Studies combined with one of: Archaeology, Biology, Economics, Economics & Social History, English, History, Language, Maths, Music, Philosophy, Politics, Physics, Sociology (all non QTS); short courses and day conferences on campus and school-based INSET and consultancy.

PARTNERSHIPS

The Department has strong links with the City of York Education Service and with schools in the city and the surrounding areas. These support active partnerships for ITT, CPD, research and curriculum development. Internationally the Department has active links in Japan, Taiwan and Southern Africa and participates in a number of EU networks.

MAIN RESEARCH AND DEVELOPMENT INTERESTS

- Primary School Education
- Science Education
- Teachers & Teaching

OTHER SPECIAL FEATURES

The Northern Office of NFER is attached to the Department.